NEW IDEAS FOR

SCIENCE
FAIR
PROJECTS

*By Roger Williams Sawyer
and Robert A. Farmer*

New York

Published by ARCO PUBLISHING COMPANY, Inc.
219 Park Avenue South, New York, N.Y. 10003

Library of Congress Catalog Card Number 67–10992
Arco Catalog Number 1538

Manufactured in the United States of America
by American Book–Stratford Press, Inc.

Contents

Part III   PROJECT REPORTS

Introduction

By Joseph H. Kraus, Coordinator
International Science Fair

SATISFYING the creative urge, finding the key to open the doors to new adventures and discoveries, exploring the unknown, are pursuits which have intrigued man since he first appeared on earth.

Pre-college youth today find the same challenges offered through a relatively "new" approach to learning generally listed as "the project method," but more easily recognized as the Science Fair.

The word "new" is quoted because it is not new at all. It is merely a different emphasis, which makes it smart to stretch the imagination into many areas. Encouragement and motivation have become greater through the active participation of adults who would have steered clear of any involvement only a generation or so ago.

If we go back in history to the ancient Greeks, we learn that the ratio of the circumference of a circle to its diameter (pi) was given as 3. Even the Old Testament quotes this figure when it describes Solomon's Temple as "ten cubits from one rim to the other" and adds that a "line of thirty cubits did compass around it" (I Kings 7). Early philosophers argued this relationship for years on end. Then someone rolled a marked cylinder on a surface and established a somewhat more precise figure of 3⅐. Even today we do not know the relationship exactly. Pi still is an irrational number, even though it has been computed to 2,037 decimal places the first ten of which are 3.1415926536.

Thus it happened that, even in earliest times, either the truth of theories or concepts was established by irrefutable evidence, or these concepts and theories were discarded upon evidential negation.

During the early days of "wireless," as radio was called, we used a Ford spark coil to pump energy into a four-wire antenna, put a nonelectric flat-

1

iron on the key, carried our 24″ x 36″ "portable" receiver with its five-foot-high loading coils to some nearby tree, threw a wire over a branch, and tried to listen to our own signal. At that time, those who played around with this were looked upon as "screwballs." We "were wasting our time," "were fooling around with silly gadgets," "could have put our talents to better advantage," etc. Other youngsters, and oldsters for that matter, who tried to breed tropical fish, were paving their own road to some mental institution.

Yet, in their prime, our own fathers built wire mesh cages, raised moths and butterflies from eggs, fed the caterpillars daily, provided places for the chrysalides, then killed and mounted the specimens at the instant that the wings were fully expanded, and either placed the creatures in exhibit cases, swapped them with other enthusiasts, or made lastingly beautiful "nature scenes" using the butterflies, dried plants, and flowers. From such tomfoolery came our deForests, Hazeltines, Goldsmiths, Andreas, Teslas, without whom none of the things so commonplace today would have been in existence. From them, too, came our entomologists, geneticists, and medical greats.

Doubtless the first science fair in the United States was started by the American Institute of the City of New York, a nonprofit institution chartered by New York State Legislature in 1828 to promote science, invention, and industry. On its one hundredth anniversary, in 1928, the Institute launched the first Children's Science Fair. Confining its activities at first to an area of fifty miles from Times Square, the Institute expanded its field of operation with the opening of the New York World's Fair, 1939–40. In a Student's Science Laboratory in the Westinghouse Building, pre-college students demonstrated their familiarity with laboratory instruments and techniques. Around the walls of this laboratory were many science exhibits made by students from kindergarten grades up. The school science clubs, junior academies of science, Christmas lectures, and many other programs were a natural outgrowth of the over-all effort.

However, the real impetus to the science youth program occurred when Science Service of Washington, D.C., the nonprofit institution for the popularization of science, assumed the national expansion of these pioneering efforts. In 1950, it launched a National Science Fair, which soon became International. Today, science fairs are operating in some forty foreign countries. Truly, a science fair can be successful anywhere in the world, regardless of the level of education of the students and regardless of available equipment. The youngster who asks "why?", who longs to know, who wants to explore, who seeks to probe, can use his native intelligence, the materials he has on hand, or can borrow or purchase, and complete a self-assigned challenge on schedule. The end result becomes a worthy exhibit.

Personal motivations are as varied as the participants themselves. There is no certainty of financial reward, but the joy of accomplishment cannot be measured in dollars and cents. The molding of the mind to think critically and creatively, to tie together information and observation, to give meaning to premises and consequences, becomes an asset that the student never loses. Such a mind is quick to appreciate the major contributions of teachers, science fair directors, scientists, and many others too numerous to mention.

Regardless of what you do, your performance always will be compared with that of your peers. This is also true in science fairs. But while scientist judges try to be fair in their evaluations, they are not infallible. And although everyone strives to win (no one ever enters any competition with the hope of losing), the greatest values come through active participation.

You who read this book should remember that a piece of this world is yours. Whether you seek it under the microscope, at the bottom of the sea, in the fields, inside the mountains, out in space, or in a laboratory, is a choice that only you can make. Today, top scientists are ready to inspire you with the same gratification they experience from their callings. If other students of your own age can reach out and grasp a piece of this world, so can you. It is there for the taking. All you need to do is reach a little farther, then keep on reaching as you continue to progress.

Joseph H. Kraus, Coordinator
International Science Fair

PART I

Planning and Executing
Your Project

CHAPTER 1

Science
and the Science Fair

SCIENCE is an adventure. The imagination, creativity, and care that go into a research project are matched by the excitement that such a project can generate. It is the essence of a research project that the results are unknown; a feeling of excitement and adventure accompanies this exploration into the unforeseen.

When you are learning science in school, you may often find it difficult to relate your studies to the "real" world, the world beyond the classroom. How will the dissection of a frog, the preparation of hydrogen, or a demonstration of wave mechanics stand to help you in the pursuit of a scientific or any other career? What relationship is there between the dry, seemingly standardized laboratory experiments and the work which leads to the exciting scientific discoveries being made today? Certainly, a gap does exist between the school laboratory and the world of science; but one excellent means of bridging that gap is available to you. That means is the SCIENCE FAIR!

Science fairs are held for the purpose of letting students work on scientific projects all their own, projects that are carried on apart from academic requirements. The fact that schools encourage science fair participation does not mean that the student's project is not completely his own. A key word in science-fairing is "independence." Planning and executing your own science fair project will give you a taste of what it would be like to devote yourself to a scientific career. At the science fair, you compete with fellow student scientists, and your work is judged by leading adult scientists; through participating, you are given a clear, exciting picture of the scientific life outside of school.

The Scientific Life

Science is a mysterious compound of many essential factors, all equally difficult to pinpoint for discussion. Three components are clearly necessary: hard work, inspiration, and luck.

Almost everyone is familiar with the story of Dr. Alexander Fleming and his discovery of penicillin. While he was otherwise engaged, a stray spore drifted through Fleming's laboratory window and alighted upon a nourishing culture. Fleming returned to the culture, examined it, and discovered the new mold, which he called penicillin. Here, certainly, the element of luck played a part in one of the great discoveries of all time. Yet, after his discovery, Dr. Fleming wrote, "If my mind had not been in a reasonably perceptive state, I might not have paid any attention to it. I might have been in a bad temper . . . or I might have been suffering from the after-effects of too heavy a meal and been mentally too sluggish to notice it or do anything about it. . . . Before you can notice anything strange happening, you have got to be a good workman, a master of your craft."* The successful scientist must be a diligent, competent observer, able to utilize the little clues that Nature gives him, which may lead to scientific achievement.

The element of good fortune puts important scientific discoveries within the grasp of any diligent researcher. Charles Goodyear worked for many years in an attempt to discover a method to make rubber impervious to heat and cold. Along the way, he discovered that he could remove the stickiness from rubber with either magnesium or quicklime solution, but by 1837 he had made no progress toward his primary goal. In that year he purchased the rights to an imperfect process for making rubber heat-resistant and concentrated upon improving that process. Of his efforts, he wrote, "I was encouraged . . . by the reflection that what is hidden and unknown, and cannot be discovered by scientific research, will most likely be discovered by accident, if at all. . . ."† And, in fact, Goodyear's discovery was accidental. Since his wife had long been tired of his endless experimentation with rubber, he was able to experiment only when she was away. One day in February, 1839, he was at work when he heard his wife returning. Hurriedly, Goodyear hid the mixture in the hot kitchen oven. Hours later, he retrieved the rubber, examined it, and found, to his amazement, that the substance was heat-resistant, cold-resistant, and solid. Goodyear had discovered vulcanization—by chance.

Today, a favorable environment is provided for both chance discovery and controlled observation in the large and well-organized institutions where

---

* Quoted in Egon Larsen, *Men Who Shaped the Future* (New York: Roy Publishers, 1954), p. 133.

† *Ibid.*, p. 69.

much of our scientific research is carried on. The research facilities offered by these centers are useful tools to the scientist, and the working atmosphere there is excellent. Yet it is the individual scientist who is indispensable to the research center; it is his *inspiration* upon which an institution must depend for its accomplishments.

In science nowadays, one often hears, matters have become too complex for any great breakthroughs to be made by young scientists working alone. Could a student today develop a science fair project worthy of notice throughout the scientific world?

Dr. Edwin Land, at the age of nineteen, had made such a startling discovery that he found it necessary to withdraw from school in order to devote himself to scientific pursuits.

While still in high school, Land had worked extensively with lenses and the physics of light, a study that he expected to continue at Harvard. Instead, he withdrew from college, perfected his new lens, and formed a corporation to produce the lens and to carry on research in related fields. In 1941, Land culminated his researches by developing the Polaroid-Land camera. Land's success may be traced to confidence in his own inspiration, which led him to sacrifice his academic career for the development of the idea in which he believed.

Fleming, Goodyear, Land: through their efforts, three exciting discoveries in science. Fleming found penicillin while engaged in routine work; Goodyear had long sought a process that would make rubber commercially usable, but happened on vulcanization totally by chance; Land followed an inspiration, born of diligence, that led him to the polaroid lens. The three shared one trait—hard work. Each of these young men adhered to the *scientific method;* that is, each followed a carefully ordered scheme of research and experimentation, according to which every action was planned and noted; every result, observed, recorded, and analyzed.

The Scientific Method

The scientific method is the framework upon which a research project should be built. No one description of what constitutes the scientific method will meet with universal acceptance, but for most purposes the procedures of the method can be divided into three large categories: HYPOTHESIS, EXPERIMENT, and CONCLUSION. Each of these categories can, of course, be subdivided many times over.

The basis of a scientific research project is the HYPOTHESIS, or working theory, usually formulated before the actual experimentation is begun, which provides the direction for the project. Many factors should be considered as you devise your own hypothesis.

First, you must be able to describe the *facts* with which you are working in such a way that they will be comprehensible both to you and to others. In order to make this description easily available to all, and to facilitate the relation of your findings to the findings of others, your subject matter must be *classified* or *systematized*. This is a very important step in the process of building the hypothesis; in fact, an entire branch of science, taxonomy, is devoted to it.

Description, systematization, and often measurement, are necessary merely because they allow you to deal with information in an orderly way. The next step is to construct from this information a theory, or hypothesis, which states what your project is expected to discover. Your hypothesis will stand or fall upon the quality of your analysis of the information that you have assimilated.

Not all projects require a formulated hypothesis at this point, however; sometimes a hypothesis is not established until the experiment has been concluded. And for some projects—such as collections—no hypothesis at all is required.

EXPERIMENT depends most heavily upon *observation*. Observation, by itself, is a basic element in nonexperimental, as well as experimental, science projects. Uncontrolled observation, which takes place outside the laboratory, may include anything from documenting the ecology of a pond to living with apes for several years, as did one noted anthropologist, Jane Goodall. Uncontrolled observation, of course, is less precise than experimental observation, for which very exact recording of specific experimental happenings is required.

In order to reduce the possibility of obtaining misleading results (which can occur even when your facts were recorded precisely), *repetition* and *consensus* are essential procedures. If you obtain the same experimental results repeatedly, you will be more sure that you have not accepted inaccurate results brought about by chance.

Control over the experimental environment is a necessity for experimentation. You must attempt to record all variables and account for their effects upon the results attained. In comparative experiments, care must be taken to insure that the environment does not change from one experiment to another. Changed conditions of which the scientist is not aware, such as varying degrees of purity of different sources of the same chemical, or mere temperature changes, can sometimes affect experimental results. It is imperative to control as many variables as is possible.

After meticulously recording your experimental results, you proceed to the third major step of the scientific method—the CONCLUSION. Forming your conclusion, on the basis of the experimental data that you have acquired (and the knowledge gained from your research), would seem to be, at first glance, a comparatively simple task. This first glance, however, is deceptive. It is not enough merely to state your conclusion; the conclusion must be substantiated by evidence gathered from the substance of the project. If it has not been properly explained, a worthwhile project can fail to have any influence upon the scientific world. A science fair project, when poorly presented, is apt to pass unrecognized, regardless of the skill and success of the experimentation.

The importance of the scientific method cannot be overemphasized. To understand why it is so important, one must comprehend the nature of science. Science builds upon itself; its continual growth is the result of the new discoveries being made in every field. If a researcher in New Mexico wishes to know the physical properties of a certain alloy, his first step will be to search the documented information available to him for any record of that alloy's physical properties. Let us suppose that this alloy has already been studied, and certain of its physical properties defined, by a scientist in Connecticut. To the New Mexico researcher, however, this study will be of no value as a scientific contribution unless its results are well documented, intelligible, and available to him.

The Science Fair

This year more than one million grade school, junior high, and high school students will participate in *science fairs*. Just what is a science fair?

Science fairs vary greatly in size and content. They may be large or small, the projects entered may be specialized or generalized, and the level of achievement represented may be sophisticated or elementary. Mr. Joseph H. Kraus, Coordinator of the International Science Fair (and of its predecessor, the National Science Fair-International, since its inception in 1950), defines a science fair as ". . . a collection of exhibits designed by students of precollege age. Each exhibit is designed to show a biological, physical, chemical, or technical principle, a laboratory or other procedure, an industrial development, or an orderly collection of anything which may be fitted into the broad concept of any branch of pure or applied science."*

Science fairs as we know them today had their beginning in 1928, when the American Institute of the City of New York organized what it called the Childrens' Science Fair. The science-fair idea caught on during the 1930's. In 1941, the Science Service of Washington, D.C., like the American Institute a nonprofit organization, took charge of the coordination of science fairs. Under its direction, Science Clubs of America grew rapidly, science fairs became even more widespread, and the Westinghouse Science Talent Search was inaugurated. Nineteen-fifty saw the first National Science Fair,

---

* Quoted in *Ideas for Science Fair Projects* (5th ed.; New York: Arco Publishing Company, 1965); p. 12.

Science Service

Top: View of part of the exhibit area of the 1963 National Science Fair-International (now the International Science Fair) at Albuquerque, New Mexico. *Bottom:* Science fair winners and judges are fêted at the Health Awards Banquet at the University of New Mexico.

with a total of thirty student exhibitors. In 1966, in Dallas, over four hundred exhibitors took part in the seventeenth annual International Science Fair.

The International Science Fair today is the apex of a pyramidal structure of science fairs throughout the country and overseas. The base of the pyramid is formed by the smallest fairs: the local senior high school and similar fairs. Winners at the senior high school fairs, and in many cases all others who so choose, are invited to exhibit their projects at regional fairs, where they compete with students from other schools in their area. In most cases, the regional fairs send their winners directly to the International Science Fair; in some instances, the regional fair leads to a state fair, and the state fair winners go to the International. In Massachusets, the state fair and the International are often held concurrently, and the sponsors of the regional fair must decide to which fair they will send their winners.

Science fairs are not limited to those affiliated with the International Science Fair. Many independent science fairs exist for the purpose of allowing the interested student to create and exhibit his project. Any science fair represents a worthwhile opportunity for you to demonstrate your initiative and capabilities, although a fair with International Science Fair affiliation offers the most demanding competition to the ambitious young scientist.

The structure of the science fair will be fully described in Part II. Of general interest, however, is the fact that science fairs today exist not only at the high school, regional, and national levels, but also at junior high and grammar school levels. In nearly every case, science fairs are arranged so that boys compete only with boys, and girls with girls. Thus two prizes are awarded on each level and in each category; one for the winning boy and a similar prize for the winning girl.

At the heart of any science fair are the projects that compose it. Science fairs exist only to display and evaluate these projects, which are the end results of the students' labors.

Projects can begin in the classroom, in school science clubs, or at home. They are frequently planned far in advance of the intended exhibition. Some science fairs merely exhibit the different projects (this is more common where the exhibitors are younger), but most involve competition and judging. Projects are judged on a comparative basis by educators and scientists in the community.

The success of your project (any project that you carry through to completion satisfactorily may be termed a successful project) is often determined by the correct choice of topic for your research. A good selection of topic will give you a project objective that is both attainable and interesting enough to spur you on to complete the project. If you haven't done a science project before, the choice of a topic may not come easily to you. It is an important choice, as you will soon see.

CHAPTER 2

Choosing a Topic

CHOOSING a topic for your project is often the most crucial step in your entire science fair effort. Imagine the student who finds, to his chagrin, that his chosen project is too ambitious for him to be able to complete it in time for the fair. Or think how you would feel if you discovered, too late, as the date of the science fair approached, that you could easily have tackled a more exacting project, one with a better chance of being a winner.

Let us not mislead you, however. Degree of difficulty is not the only factor that you must consider when making your choice of topic. Time, expense, collateral reading, necessary resources, availability of advice on critical points of the experimentation: all these factors must be taken into account before you decide on a specific project. But even before you can undertake to consider these factors, you must have in mind a general *topic idea*.

Your Interests

Choosing a topic idea is essentially a matter of pinpointing wherein your interests lie. You will find that numerous topic ideas will occur to you if you alert yourself to the vast opportunities for research and experimentation with which your everyday life presents you. For example, a girl from Virginia became curious about the inability of a garbage disposal unit to grind onion skins. She made a paper-like substance from onion skins and experimented with the new material's physical properties. Her science fair project, based upon this experimentation, was a recent winner at the International Science Fair.

Perhaps you are finding it difficult to hit upon a topic idea that seems certain to develop into a worthwhile research project. To what sources can

14

you turn to discover an idea in which you can place your confidence? Here
are some suggestions: try your hobbies; look through the scientific news
media; during classroom discussion or lab periods, keep alert for any mention of a subject of interest; and, most important, evaluate all unusual or
interesting happenings in terms of their suitability for a potential topic.

Any of your *hobbies* may be an excellent source of topic ideas that will
hold your attention. Since your hobby is something which you have taken
up on your own and to which you devote a continuing interest, any topic
idea that it yields will most likely be a successful one.

Many hobbies are especially pregnant with possibilities for science fair
projects. A tropical-fish devotee, for instance, might become very interested
in the bacteria and other parasites that cause diseases in tropical fish. He
could build a project around this interest by experimenting with various
substances to find antidotes to these diseases. Or he might study different
forms of the organisms under the microscope to determine their reproductive
cycles. Or our fish fancier could carry out experiments in behavioral psychology with his fish.

If photography happens to be your hobby, you may be inspired to delve
into the scientific principles that govern the developing of film. Perhaps you
spend some of your time in gardening; then a study of the effects of specific
chemicals or soil conditions on plant growth could be your beginning. A
local fair not so long ago produced a study of the effects of radiation and
microwaves on rice. Opportunities are unlimited, and nearly any preoccupa-
tion can, with some thought, provide the basis for a good science fair topic.

The *scientific news media* may help you to tie in a specific interest (such
as your tropical fish, for example) with an idea for a topic. Scanning the recent issues of magazines such as *Scientific American, Time, Popular Mechanics, Mechanix Illustrated,* and *Popular Science* will give you access to
many of the exciting new developments in science, several of which may be
applicable in some way to your area of interest.

In your *school science courses,* you will be exposed to numerous ideas for
potential science fair projects. During classroom discussion, while carrying
out laboratory experiments, or at meetings of extracurricular science clubs,
many exciting questions are raised. You, of course, are the best judge of
what seems capable of holding your attention over an extended period of
time. If you keep a receptive mind, you will soon learn to weed out the less
interesting topics and recognize others that are worthy of serious consideration.

Look at all daily occurrences in the light of their suitability for topic ideas.
Here we are reminded of the onion skin's refusal to be ground up in the
garbage disposal. Topic ideas do not always come so easily, but the fact
that they may crop up where least expected is indisputable. Magazine and
newspaper advertisements and television and radio commercials are constantly bringing to your attention exciting scientific developments and their

practical applications. Several very good projects have been stimulated by new applications and modifications of such standard synthetic materials as nylon and rayon.

Don't lose heart if you fail to come up with a satisfactory topic immediately. Give yourself time to think, time to consider your own interests and capabilities. By the same token, if you know that a decision about your science fair project must be reached within two weeks, don't wait until the last minute. You may find yourself committed to an inferior topic, and your entire project is apt to suffer.

Let us assume that you have taken the time to examine your interests, and that you have come up with two or three (or more) topic ideas, which you feel would make top-rate science projects. How do you determine which of your ideas to adopt and which to discard?

There are many considerations, besides your own degree of interest, that enter into the determination of a good science research project. You will be wise to approach these considerations one by one, perhaps by setting up a check list to evaluate each topic idea. The most important considerations are discussed below.

Degree of Difficulty

As you are about to enter the science fair, take the time to examine your objectives. Are you willing to participate simply to gain valuable experience, so that you can enter again in subsequent years with improved projects? Or, if this year's fair is to be your last, do you intend to go all out to make it to the level of the International Science Fair? Most likely, your plans fall somewhere in between. Wherever you stand, it is important that you take note of your goal, whether it be to win or to gain experience through participating, and be sure that your project is in line with that goal.

"Don't bite off more than you can chew" is an axiom which too many science-fairers neglect. Every spring sees large numbers of mournful faces of those boys and girls who got carried away with projects that were too ambitious. Indeed, many science-fairers have dreams of glory about wonderful project ideas that will lead to magnificently successful displays. These projects are usually very advanced, terribly complex, and scientifically unsound, even though they may be exciting and creative. Some students actually complete projects like these, but they are a small minority. For the beginning science-fairer, at least, such dreams often result in unfinished or confused projects and consequent failure. Thus, it is clear that the serious science fair participant must examine his own abilities as well as his goals and interests.

The most important and realistic test of any topic is whether it is within your capabilities. Some projects simply require too much formal knowledge and experience for the average junior or senior high school student. Make an honest assessment of your abilities in relation to the *degree of difficulty* of your chosen project. Do you have the necessary academic background and skills? Have you had any practical experience in the field? Do you have a working knowledge of any laboratory techniques that may be required? The answers to questions such as these will give you an indication of your ability to cope with your project. Of course, a willingness to work hard and work long hours can overcome many an obstacle, so don't sell yourself short if you feel capable of taking on a very difficult project. But be realistic: admit to yourself that you may not be successful. Tackling a difficult project is a gamble, and a gambler must be prepared to face an occasional defeat.

Time

If you are satisfied that your topic idea is within your capabilities, *time* should be the next item on your check list. Different projects require different time allotments; this time is devoted to planning, research, setting up the project, working through it, assembling the results, and drawing a conclusion. Often, you will have to spend more time than you had originally anticipated on certain phases of the work. For example, if your project requires you to follow scientific principles and use procedures with which you are not familiar, you will have to set aside a good deal of time for research.

Some chemistry projects involve long, delicate, complicated laboratory work, the results of which can be destroyed by the slightest accident. If your project is of this type, you should allow extra time as a margin of safety for possible errors.

It is much better to overestimate your time requirements than to underestimate them. You can always utilize any extra time to improve upon the neatness and clarity of your project presentation, but there is no way to postpone the date of the science fair to allow you to complete your project. A good schedule for science fair participants to follow is: begin to think about topics during the summer, decide upon a project by the beginning of the fall academic term or soon thereafter, and start to assemble materials by the end of September. These suggested time allotments, of course, may vary according to the requirements of the project.

Much progress can be made on a science project during the summer vacation. This time of year is ideally suited for making ecological studies, assembling collections, conducting cave and geological explorations, and many other activities. In fact, devoting a summer to project work can mean a healthy start for almost any type of undertaking, since you will have enough time to develop your project before getting tied up in other school activities.

Materials

Just as you must consider your personal resources when selecting a topic, so, too, should you think about your *material resources*. Do you have the facilities necessary for research and project development? If not, can you obtain them easily? A primary consideration at this point is the amount of money that you intend to spend on your project. It is imperative that you make an estimate of the total cost of your experiment before you begin work. Make sure that you will be able to cover this cost before allowing your topic idea to bloom into a project. There are numerous procedures for keeping your expenses to a minimum, and these will be discussed at length in Chapter 3.

Suppose your project calls for the utilization of X rays upon mice. You may have to obtain access to a radiation laboratory; you may even find it necessary to have a technician do the radiating for you. But many students have successfully completed projects requiring radiation by applying to dentists, doctors who have X-ray equipment, or hospitals. There are also other types of radiation, such as light, electricity at high frequency, and laser. Whatever technique you decide to use, be sure to make any necessary arrangements prior to committing yourself to this particular experiment. Your project will certainly fall flat on its face if, after you have taken all the preliminary steps, you find that you are not able to obtain permission to do the radiation treatments.

Guidance

One of the general categories in which projects may be submitted at the International Science Fair is Physics. Although some attempts are being made to introduce this subject at the elementary and junior high school levels, at present the majority of students begin the study of physics in high school. Even at this level, however, a single year of physics is the rule rather than the exception; thus, a project in this area might very well require a great deal of self-taught knowledge, gained through diligent research. Learning physics, mathematics, chemistry, or any science on your own is quite a task, and an effort of which anyone can be proud. If you undertake such a task, one thing you can be sure of is that you will occasionally require *guidance*.

One of the project descriptions in Part III describes the success of transplants on mice treated by radiation. For this experiment it was necessary to study the technique of skin grafting in order to do the transplants. The

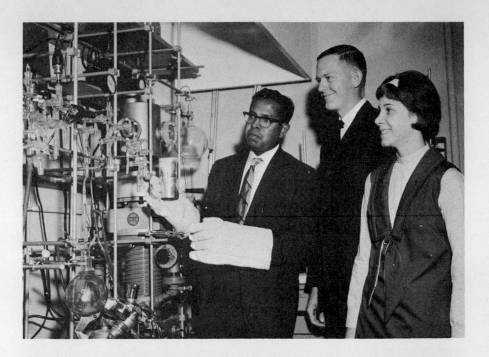

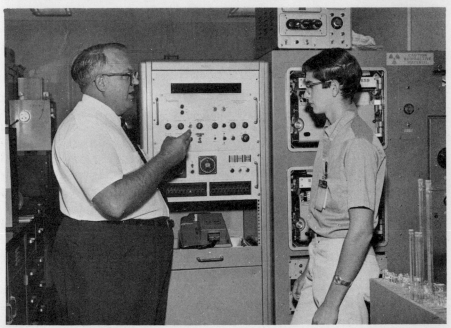

Scientists at government installations, such as the National Aeronautics and Space Administration, are usually glad to consult with students on specific aspects of research. Photographs on this page were taken in the NASA's Ames Research Center in Moffett Field, California.

student learned the technique with the guidance of a local surgeon, unknown to the experimenter prior to her project but whom she sought out well enough in advance of the actual grafting to insure the success of the experiment. It would have been seriously imperiled had this girl not sought guidance at that point. In the same manner you gravely imperil your project when you fail to assure yourself, from the outset, of adequate guidance in the area of your experimentation.

The importance of consultation cannot be overstated. Even if you have a topic completely blocked out, and have definitely decided to do your science fair project on that particular subject, be sure to consult your teachers or other professionals about it. Their long experience will usually enable them to point out at least one or two points which you may not yet have considered. If it is at all possible, do not begin the actual work on your project before you have discussed your topic from many angles with several experienced people. Discussion will help to clarify the project in your own mind, and the guidance which others can give you may save you many hours of fruitless labor.

The Nature of the Project: Winner or Loser?

Part III of this book is made up of a number of project descriptions written by First and Second Award winners at the International Science Fair. Their projects represent the cream of the science fair crop. Inasmuch as your ultimate goal as a science fair participant is, most likely, to be among the top winners, the descriptions in Part III are necessary reading for you. (Coincidentally, you will probably find Part III the most exciting section of the book.) Reading the individual stories of winning projects will give you the opportunity to share, at first hand, the planning, development, and presentation of *successful* science fair projects. None of the reports is like any other; each has its own peculiar emphasis and, thus, each holds a lesson for you.

When you have decided on a project in which you are interested, and when all the signs point to your being able to complete it to your satisfaction, then it is time to examine your project according to one other very important criterion: its *winning potential*.

We may seem to be getting ahead of ourselves at this point, since the judging of a project is the last step to take place. But the science fair participant must look ahead and should be aware of all that it takes to make a good project a winning one.

Remember: although a topic idea may be of interest to you, others may not find your completed project interesting. Both the judges and the audiences look at the projects with great care, and their examination can usually unmask any aspect of a project that is unnecessary, superficial, or uncreative. The best way to avoid a presentation that will be judged as poor is to keep the standards of judging firmly in mind when you are beginning work on your project.

Most science fairs follow the lead of the International Science Fair rather closely in regard to the judging of exhibits. ISF judging is done on a point-scale basis, according to the following criteria:

I.   Creative Ability   *30 points*
     How much of the work appears to show originality of approach or handling? Judge that which appears to you to be original regardless of the expense of purchased or borrowed equipment. Give weight to ingenious uses of materials, if present. Consider collections creative if they serve a purpose.

II. Scientific Thought   *30 points*
     Does the exhibit disclose organized procedures? Is there a planned system, classification, accurate observation, or controlled experiment? Does exhibit show a verification of laws or a cause and effect, or does it present by models or other methods a better understanding of scientific facts or theories? Give weight to probable amount of real study and effort which is represented in the exhibit. Guard against discounting for what might have been added, included, or improved.

III. Thoroughness   *10 points*
     Score here how completely the story is told. It is not essential that step-by-step elucidation of construction details be given in working models.

IV. Skill   *10 points*
     Is the workmanship good? Under normal working conditions, is the exhibit likely to demand frequent repairs? In collections, how skilled is the handling, preparation, mounting, or other treatment?

V.   Clarity   *10 points*
     In your opinion, will the average person understand what is being displayed? Are guide marks, labels, and descriptions spelled correctly, and neatly but briefly presented? Is there sensible progression of the attention of the spectator across or through the exhibit?

VI. Dramatic Value   *10 points*
     Is this exhibit more attractive than others in the same field? Do not be influenced by "cute" devices—lights, buttons, switches, cranks, or other gadgets—which contribute nothing to the exhibit.

"Creative ability" and "scientific thought" together represent 60 percent of the basis on which your exhibit is to be judged. When they are studying an exhibit, science fair judges must ask themselves whether that project is genuinely original. How heavily does it draw upon previous work in the field? Is it merely a repetition of a well-known experiment or a reiteration of knowledge already accepted by science? Does the project in question attack a scientific problem from a new and fruitful angle? If your project has been done before, then it is no longer original—unless you can *modify* the previous experimental results. At this point you may wish to remind yourself of the purpose of a scientific research project. Its objective is to contribute to the over-all store of scientific knowledge. Your project can do

Top: "Variation and Speciation of New England Butterflies" was a collection, classification, and display project of sufficiently high caliber to take its creator, Marc Roth, to the ISF. *Bottom:* This student's interest in magnetism led him to study the effect of magnetic fields upon phosphor formation.

this in only two ways: it can explore previously unexplored areas; or it can add to existing knowledge, as by refuting the results of a past experiment.

Suppose that you had planned to build a Van de Graaff generator, but have now realized that this project would not show sufficient creativity to earn you an award at your local science fair. What should your next step be? You might use the generator for testing, treatment, destruction, or creation of isotopes.

A good method of finding an original topic is to take a previous experiment or development and add a new twist to it. The derivation of exciting new plastics, for example, only provides the impetus for further research, directed toward the discovery of still more plastics compounds. The fact that one antibody has been tested on mice as a cancer-curing drug should not overshadow the fact that thousands of potential cancer-arresting drugs may have heretofore gone untested. Each year the Food and Drug Administration accepts many new medicines that have undergone testing for comparatively short periods of time and in standard ways; for your project, you might test one of these drugs by administering it in a previously untried way, such as to single-celled animals, viruses, or plants, or to specific organs of animals.

Within each science there are nooks and crannies into which time has not yet permitted exploration. Every bit of knowledge gained is a step forward, however, and if your project does not fill in one of these nooks, then, perhaps, it will have given you the background from which you can strive more successfully in the future to add to science's store of knowledge.

Hopefully, your planned project is now interesting; within your capabilities; unhampered by lack of time, materials, or availability of guidance; and *original!* If it is all of these, your project is acceptable, and you can begin work on it. A word about safety is in order at this point.

Safety

It is unhappily not uncommon to read of young people who have been seriously burned or otherwise injured by chemical explosions. An essential feature of the study of science is learning to conduct dangerous experiments in *safety*. We rarely read of professional scientists having serious accidents, yet the amount of experimentation done by professionals in this country is phenomenal. You must not undertake any experiment that is potentially dangerous to yourself or others without the active guidance of a professional man well versed in your area of study.

Most science fairs prohibit the display of dangerous chemicals, open flames, explosives, and live, poisonous reptiles. Disqualification is the penalty for failing to abide by this rule.

CHAPTER 3

You're On Your Way!

BEFORE making the final selection of your intended science fair topic, you will be wise to do some preliminary research in the area to determine its difficulty and its characteristics, and to let you estimate the extra research that will be required. Once you have made your final topic choice, with the help of this information, it is time to begin the real research.

Research

Research may be either generalized or specialized. Obviously, the degree of specialization of your research will depend upon your chosen topic. It may deal with an entire field of science or it may touch only upon various aspects of the field. Before attempting any specialized research, you will often find it necessary to have a firm general knowledge of your field of study.

If you are just starting out as an exhibitor in science fairs, your best bet is probably to learn as much about your chosen area as time permits. You may not be able to incorporate all your knowledge into one project, but you will be acquiring the background for substantially improved projects in later years.

If you are a science fair veteran, then you know the value of the thirty points that judges award for "scientific thought." You know that, as the judges question you about your project, they will be trying to discover not only how well you understand your project, but *how well you understand the scientific principles behind the success of your project.* There is rarely a project that scientific research cannot improve; but there is, unfortunately, a limit to your available time for research. You must budget your time wisely between specialized and generalized research, remembering that, as

24

specialized research is required for the project's completion, so, too, is general research necessary for total understanding. To explain the *significance* of your work to the judges, you must be familiar with the scientific area in which you are working.

There is at least one other motivation for acquiring a wide background in your entire field of research, one which is especially crucial in the case of the more ambitious topics. In order to give your experimentation a clear direction, you must know the lay of the scientific land and the course you wish to plot. You may be attracted by the leisure and freedom of undirected research, but such research will not help you to meet science fair deadlines. Organizing a handful of miscellaneous data is time-consuming and needless; moreover, the result usually yields only a small percentage of *useful* information.

The best method of acquiring a general background in your field is by taking a course in the area of science concerned. It is difficult to do a project in physics or electronics prior to studying physics, or to carry out an advanced mathematical project without the benefit of calculus. But such projects are attempted often enough! A junior high school student anxious to create his own science fair project does not have to look far to find topic ideas in chemistry, biology, zoology, perhaps even in elementary physics, which will develop into excellent projects.

As you begin your program of study on your topic, you will be faced with any number of sources of information. You must select a beginning point for your research.

The School Library

The first place to look for material is, of course, your school library, since it will be the most convenient. School libraries, as a rule, contain information of a generalized nature. However, they also contain leads to information of a more specific character in their bibliographies and periodical and book references.

Don't be afraid to consult an encyclopedia for specialized information. Some high school libraries have, in addition to standard encyclopedias, scientific reference books or encyclopedias. These, too, can provide you with leads to more technical books and monographs.

Other Libraries

In all likelihood, you will have to go beyond your school library to other libraries, not as accessible as your school's, but well worth the inconvenience of traveling to them. They offer invaluable opportunities for specialized research. Your community library will carry many more periodicals than does the school library, and its books will delve more deeply into specific areas of research.

Many scientific and technical societies maintain entire libraries devoted to one field. You might find out more about these libraries by inquiring of your science teachers and of your school and community librarians. Admittance to these libraries is usually restricted. However, as scientists are more than willing to aid industrious students, you should not have difficulty in obtaining special permission to use whatever library you require.

You will find that many technical libraries have specialized classification schemes. Don't be afraid to take your questions directly to the librarian. He is trained to keep a sharp eye on incoming material and can frequently draw your attention to literature dealing with new developments and trends with which you were not familiar.

A college or university library is a gold mine. You can most probably move right in and complete the majority of your research in that one location. Since library privileges are usually restricted, write to the head librarian or library director regarding permission to use the library's facilities. Include a note from a science teacher attesting to your serious concern with research.

A good number of science fair projects require only *library research*. There is no reason for you to feel that your project is inadequate merely because you did not have to search beyond the libraries for your information. However, some science research projects require information that cannot be found in libraries. There is then no alternative but to look further for your information.

Personal Consultation

A source that can often prove as valuable as printed information is personal consultation. You will find that most people who are able to help you will be perfectly willing to do so. Your first recourse should probably be to your teachers, since they are most accessible and are very often experienced in science project guidance. Having kept an eye on your project from its inception, they will have a more than casual interest in your work and should be able to give you both solid advice in your field and excellent references to printed material and to other people who can help you.

Professional scientists, technicians, engineers, doctors, and college professors are usually quite willing to talk with students about some specific aspect of research. In Washington, D.C., for example, the Joint Board on Science Education has in operation a program in which a scientist, called a "contact member," is assigned to every school in this twenty-five-mile area.

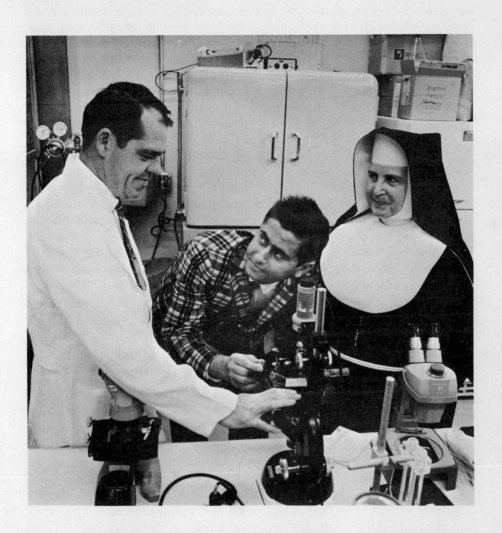

A scientist at NASA's Ames Research Center demonstrates apparatus to visitors.

This scientist may be consulted throughout the week, day or night, by students engrossed in their projects. Be sure to make appointments with professional men well in advance, for their time is limited. And, make sure that *you,* yourself, are prepared for the interview.

Letters can be as productive for you as personal interviews. If your request is for quite specific information, addressing it to a scientist in the form of a letter may be even simpler than attempting to set up an interview. Industrial concerns often maintain information services, which are best approached through letters.

Be sure to get started writing letters and arranging for personal interviews well in advance of the time when you will need the information, since delayed responses and postponed interviews are always a possibility.

Your Project Notebook

As you are beginning your research, you should also begin to record your progress on the project. It is of the essence of the scientific method that every research project must be well documented; it is this painstaking documentation which allows one scientist to build upon the works of others. If you wish the results of your work to be lasting, you must make your project live in your notebook. And, what is more to the point, if you wish to be a science fair winner, a project notebook is essential.

Your project notebook is a means of assembling information. A tablet, a set of file cards, or a loose-leaf binder will be sufficient for the purpose. It is necessary that you try to keep a running account of everything that concerns the project—observations, speculation, experiments, materials, expenses, procedures, data, hypotheses, and conclusions.

Keeping a notebook on a day-to-day basis can be a nerve-racking occupation if you attempt to keep it highly organized. Don't let a disarranged notebook worry you. Your goal is to document the progress of your experiment, not to keep a neat notebook. Concentrate only on recording the information; think about organizing it when you have completed your project.

Note Taking and Filing

A word of advice on note taking is in order. It is not hard to get yourself fouled up, if you are using a haphazard system of collecting information from varied sources. The more notes you take, the greater the risk that you will end up with an unmanageable conglomeration of facts.

A good way to avoid this hazard is to take notes on file cards. These are easily manageable and, if filed properly, give you the quickest access to the information which you have acquired. When you are taking notes, identify your source clearly at the top of the card. Then, if you have occasion to refer to your research in your final project report, you will have at your fingertips the proper citation for reference. Finally, always be certain that the subject of your note is evident at the top of the card, and file that card by subject. In this way, you will save yourself from having to leaf through all your notes to find one specific bit of information; you will be able to turn directly to the desired card.

Research is almost solely your responsibility; thus, the amount of information that comes your way depends more on you than on anyone else. Most people are glad to help aspiring scientists—all you have to do is ask.

CHAPTER 4

Executing Your Project

THE manner of execution of your project will depend greatly on your topic and on the type of project that you have decided to do. One topic may often be treated in several different ways. Suppose that you intended to study vitamin deficiencies. You might attempt to *discover* what natural conditions cause certain foods to be deficient in one or another vitamin; you could *treat* vitamin deficiency through biochemical analysis; or you could attempt to *induce* a vitamin deficiency in laboratory animals. Each of these approaches to the subject of vitamin deficiencies would require significantly different conditions, amounts of time, money, materials, and research. Herein enters the urgent necessity for *planning*.

Common sense tells us that good planning will be more necessary for the project that goes right down to the wire than for the one that is expected to be completed months ahead of the science fair. The more involved your project is, the more likely it is that planning will be essential to its success. It stands to reason that a complex project will present more surprises to the experimenter than will a simpler project.

One of the projects described in Part III of this book involved research into garlic as a potential cancer-curing compound. The boy's goal was to break down garlic into its components and register their effects on cancerous mice, so as eventually to isolate whatever it was in garlic that acted to arrest cancer.

Since a concentrated garlic solution did prolong the lives of cancerous mice, the project went on in quest of the cancer-combatting ingredient. Such a quest ends only when the ingredient being sought is found. The ingredient may be the protein that is isolated and tested first, or it may be the enzyme that is the last substance to be tested. In this particular experiment, the hypothesis based upon research proved faulty. It was not

30

discovered until the garlic was almost completely broken down into its components that the RNA molecular complex was the active ingredient.

In this case, the experimenter had to *plan* for the possibility that the agent sought would be the last to be tested. This preliminary planning was necessary to insure that the project would be completed in time. Although earlier completion would have been a blessing, this project could not have been completed until the agent had been found. This does not mean that all the work preceding the discovery of the cancer-combatting factor was of no value, however. The fact that all the other components of garlic had no discernible effect on the cancerous mice was a discovery in itself. (When Thomas Edison completed seven hundred experiments, all of which were failures, his reaction was: "You now know seven hundred materials that cannot be used for the filaments of an incandescent lamp. Now try some others.") Still, if the experimenter is to have something to show for the work he has done, he must allow himself sufficient time for completion.

How to Plan

Review the list of criteria for judging, given on p. 21: creative ability, scientific thought, thoroughness, skill, clarity, and dramatic value. The first two criteria were instrumental to your choice of topic, since you wanted to have a project that showed enough originality and initiative to stand up to its competition. By the latter four criteria, the thoroughness and skill with which you perform and present your experiment are evaluated.

Merely finishing your experimentation is not necessarily sufficient. Although a project report is not required fo rentry in a science fair, it is a good idea to present one, since the judges critically examine all supporting evidence. Such a report will also contribute to your project's clarity and dramatic value, which are essential considerations in the judging of a presentation. Thus, you should be sure to devote adequate time to your report and your exhibit. You might note that, though a project report is not required for entry in a science fair, it is one of the basic requirements for the Science Talent Search.

Prepare a Timetable

During the course of your science fair project, your most trustworthy aid can be a *timetable*. This timetable should outline all the steps of your project and include a date for completion of each of these steps. You may also include a date for the beginning of each. You should draw up the timetable in the form of a chart, which you can place in a conspicuous spot, so that you can refer to it while you are working.

As you think over your topic idea, prepare a tentative timetable: estimate when you will complete your research, when you will start and complete experimentation, and when you will need specific materials. At this point you will probably not possess sufficient familiarity with your subject to be able to make very detailed plans. But this tentative timetable will give you a framework by which you can more easily assess your topic idea. Show it to your teachers, explaining your plans, and find out if they think that the project can be completed on schedule.

Once you are committed to your subject, go at the timetable in earnest. How much time must you spend on research before you will be able to begin experimentation? If guidance on special points will be necessary, how far in advance should you write to apply for interviews or to obtain special texts? What are all the materials you will require, and when and how should you procure them? How long will it take you to write your report, and when will you be able to begin work on it? Will you have time to design and build as good an exhibit as those with which it will be competing?

Only proper planning will allow you time at the end of your project for pulling together the various loose ends and making your exhibit one that can be clearly followed by any interested observer. Planning can also point up expenses hidden within your project which, if discovered at a later date, might force you to curtail your experiments or even to find another topic that will be a smaller burden on your budget.

Expense

Your ambition may be to create a project that will be able to compete with the best, but perhaps you feel that, to do so, you will have to invest in a great deal of expensive equipment and materials. You will find that this does not have to be the case. Some of the projects described in Part III were completed at a cost of less than $20.00 over a year's time; one cost only $2.50. The materials that you use will be determined by the topic you choose; it is no sacrifice of ingenuity if you can manage to do top-flight work with inexpensive or ordinary materials. And it is even easier to save on equipment. Schools will let you use their laboratory equipment free of charge, and many private laboratories will do the same for the serious student scientist.

Time

Planning your project step by step will also force you to do some serious thinking. The subject perhaps most worthy of your consideration is the *time* involved. How long do you want to spend on your project? Eight months? Four months? Perhaps you contemplate continuing to work on your project over a number of years, adding new twists and variations, as many science-fairers do. Will you be able to spend one hour a day on your science project? Some students get so totally engrossed in their experimentation that they work four and five hours daily on it. This is not forced labor; it is compelled by their intense interest in the work they are doing. Part of the value of planning is that it enables you to recognize for yourself just how much time you can devote to science.

It is axiomatic: anything that can possibly go wrong with a science fair project may indeed go wrong. Perhaps your project will encounter smooth sailing from start to finish, but it is best to be pessimistic nevertheless. If you are prepared for the worst, nothing that happens can throw you off stride.

When you plan your project, you are simply making the effort to *anticipate* and *eliminate* the most serious mistakes or accidents. Such mistakes can be eliminated if they can be foreseen; by recognizing them ahead of time, you can take steps to avoid them. Planning also lets you anticipate possible errors and allow yourself time to rectify them if they occur.

Types of Projects

Ideas for Science Fair Projects,* the forerunner to the present book, devotes an entire chapter to the four types of scientific research projects that may be exhibited at a science fair. To help you in setting up the timetable for your own project, a discussion of each of these types follows.

The four general areas are:
- Research and experimentation
- Engineering
- Collection, classification, and display
- Theoretical

If you already have a topic in mind, you can probably place it in one of these categories. If you have not as yet committed yourself to approach your topic from one particular standpoint, however, it will be worth your

---

* *Ideas for Science Fair Projects* (5th ed.; New York: Arco Publishing Company, 1965).

while to analyze the peculiar demands made upon projects in each category.

A "theoretical" project requires the most broad-based knowledge of any of the four types, as well as the clearest understanding of the research material used. On the other hand, if yours is a theoretical project, you may not need any materials or equipment in order to complete it; therefore, this type of project may be the most convenient to perform. This fact is attested to by Priscilla Chow and J. Richard Gott III, whose mathematics projects are described in Part III.

"Collection, classification, and display" is apt to be the most time-consuming of the categories. Such projects also require the most patience; and, needless to say, they put your powers of observation to the test.

Projects in the "engineering" category require mechanical aptitude. If your intention is to build a complicated device, which will represent part or all of your project, and if you lack mechanical experience, then seek advice. Be sure to allow yourself an ample *period of safety* in your timetable, in case building your project takes longer than you expect. Remember that even a project of this type will be judged by the criteria of creative ability and scientific thought. Using a new application of a scientific principle to expedite the operation of your experiment might be your objective. Joseph Leykam was a winner at the International Science Fair for the "Design and Construction of an Electron Microscope"; his creative ability and scientific thought were demonstrated in the *design* of the microscope.

"Research and experimentation" projects may call for any or all of the particular skills native to the other categories. This does not mean that projects of this type need be more difficult than others, but only that it is a category in which can be included a vast spectrum of topics. It is difficult to characterize a project in "research and experimentation" more explicitly than by saying that it adheres to the guide lines of the scientific method.

CHAPTER 5

The Finishing Touches

IT is a fair assumption that if you follow the advice given in the previous chapters, your experimentation—barring unforeseen accidents—will be a success. This does not necessarily mean that you will obtain the results that you hypothesized (often, an experiment may force the scientist to accept startling conclusions), but it does mean that your results will be well documented and experimentally sound. A well-advised choice of topic, intelligent planning, adequate research, careful workmanship, and precise documentation should insure you both the time and the resources from which to develop a worthwhile exhibit.

After devoting the better part of a year to a project, which you feel has been a success, you owe it to yourself to convince others (the judges and audiences at the science fair) of that fact. To assure yourself of doing so, you must work on the finishing touches and present your project effectively.

There is no question that a sloppy presentation can ruin a good project's chances for winning. By the same token, when an exhibit is well thought out and attractively designed, this can frequently mean the difference between victory and nonrecognition.

Your first step in planning the layout of your exhibit should be to check the rules of the science fair you are to enter. It is, in fact, a good idea to examine local rules even before beginning work on your project. It would be a shame to have your project disqualified from exhibition on some pretext. You may find, for example, that an exhibit requiring electrical current must be cleared with the sponsors by a given date prior to the fair, or that hypodermic needles and syringes cannot be exhibited, or that molds and bacterial cultures must be handled in a prescribed manner. Particularly if your exhibit contains electrical apparatus, you can be sure that there will be many local regulations pertaining to your presentation.

Another important regulation to be aware of concerns the amount of space you will be allowed in which to set up your exhibit. For example, the International Science Fair rules state that an exhibit must occupy a floor area or table space no greater than two and one half feet deep and four feet wide. Some fairs also have height restrictions. Finally, practicality recommends that your exhibit be set up between thirty and ninety inches from the floor, inasmuch as this range is the most comfortable area of vision for the average adult.

Your Exhibit

Planning your exhibit is a job in itself. First, it must be self-supporting—and sturdy! You have no guarantee that it won't be placed in the middle of an auditorium, far from a wall against which you can lean it. Furthermore, jostling crowds will be sure to put its sturdiness to the test.

Second, the exhibit must appear at once eye-catching, neat, attractive, and instructive. Materials, lettering, use of color, organization—many factors are instrumental to your project's appearance.

Finally, if your exhibit includes demonstrable parts, all of them must work. For example, if you exhibit a fuel cell that fails to give off a noticeable electric charge, your chances of copping an award will be considerably reduced. Don't count on good fortune to pull you through on the day of the exhibition; keep at your exhibit until you are sure that it will function smoothly every time.

Construction

The *booth* exhibit is the type usually chosen by science-fairers. (See illustration). A booth has the advantages of having two side walls, angled outward for easy viewing; a horizontal display space provided at table height; and a large back wall, useful for displaying the introductory message or your conclusions or for highlighting any attention-getting features of the project.

When constructing your exhibit, make sure that it will be durable. Paper products, such as artboard, may suffice for one showing, but if you expect to show the exhibit at science fairs in later years, more permanent materials will be in order. Suggested materials include: wood-fiber boards such as Masonite; plywood; Prestwood; and, for bracing, white pine. A primer coat applied to plywood helps to prevent warping.

Leave yourself time for the proper planning and construction of your exhibit. If this is your first project, you will probably find yourself making

Top: In her project in space research, Felicia Rose Tillman showed that hypothermic ("frozen") mice were able to survive at pressures that normothermic mice could not withstand. *Bottom:* Scott Jenkins applied experimentally a theory that he had developed and showed reduction in rocket drag as a result. This project won a First Award at the 17th ISF.

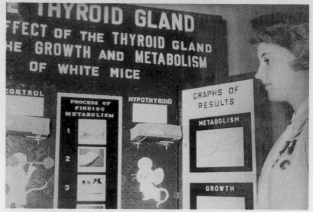

Top: In this well-designed exhibit, cartoon figures representing the experimental conclusions enliven the presentation. *Center:* Text and display elements are arranged so as to draw the viewer's eye from one side of the exhibit to the other. *Bottom:* Text is kept to a minimum, while photographs dramatize high points of the experimentation.

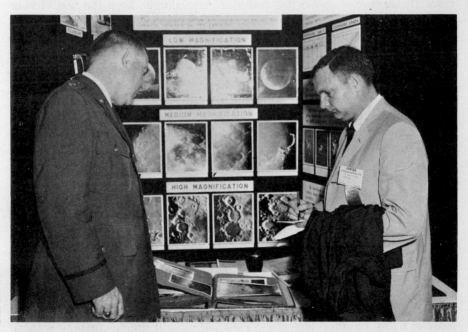

Top: Text and diagrams do not detract from the effectiveness of the apparatus, which is of major importance in this exhibit. *Bottom:* Photographs tell the story of the project with striking effect.

improvements as you go along. You may find, for instance, that a pegboard background allows you the much-needed constructional adaptability that was lacking in the standard board, which you had planned to employ.

It is wise to provide for concealed lighting on your exhibit, in order to improve its over-all appearance and readability. For this purpose, incandescent showcase lamps or even clip-on lamps will prove satisfactory. Don't forget to look into the rules on wiring at this point.

Presentation

Putting across your ideas is the main objective in this phase of your science fair project. Your experiment is complete, your display stand constructed, and all that remains is to tell the project's story in words, graphs, pictures, and demonstrations to the judges and general public. The design of your exhibit is fundamental to your success in making that story known.

Keep foremost in your mind that your experimental apparatus and/or conclusions are the key to your presentation. They are the end result of all your work on the science fair project. The remainder of your exhibit can correctly be termed supporting material. Accordingly, keep the text of your exhibit to a minimum. Text is useful for highlighting various points of the project and to provide a brief summary, but it can easily be overdone. Your project is on visual display; it is not meant to be read, as a project report is read. A picture is worth a thousand words, as the saying goes, and for a science fair exhibit that is not a bad precept to follow. (In the interests of clarity, photographs and other illustrations should be of sufficient size to let an observer view them in detail without straining.) The illustrations neatly captioned, tastefully positioned in the display. Moreover, they must used must be both meaningful and visually attractive; *i.e.*, well mounted, be able to be adequately understood by the average viewer. Many charts and tables may prove to be confusing to your audience. Be especially sure that *all* names and words are spelled correctly.

"Clarity" and "dramatic value" together represent 20 percent of the basis on which your project is judged. "Clarity" refers to the capacity of your project to make itself understood by the average person; "dramatic value," to the attractiveness of your exhibit. You can achieve clarity through careful interrelation of text and illustration. Attempt to achieve *a sensible progression of the attention of the spectator across or through the exhibit.*

It is more difficult to lay down guidelines for dramatic value. Gadgets, flashing lights, or other devices are frowned upon if they contribute nothing to the project. Yet your exhibit must stand out for its attractiveness. *Neatness* certainly is an essential ingredient of any successful exhibit. But more is required than mere neatness.

Open space can contribute greatly to an exhibit's dramatic value (as well as to its clarity). Cluttered panels only induce the viewer to pass on to the next exhibit, since the chore of unraveling the information will quickly dampen his interest in the project.

Color, when intelligently employed, will add to the dramatic value of your display. There are some general rules about the use of color that you should remember when planning your exhibit.

First, limit the number of basic colors used. One or two should be sufficient for a display of the size ordinarily presented in science fairs. From the basic colors, related shades can be drawn if more differentiation appears warranted.

Second, keep away from violent contrasts or from too much color. You are using color to highlight or contrast different areas of your project; therefore, it is secondary in your display. When color becomes primary, the display takes on an amateurish appearance. Use color only to attract, to enhance, or to point up related factors.

Know Your Project

When you take a stand at the science fair in front of your completed project, you too are on display. During the time that your project is being exhibited, it will be your function to answer questions concerning your experiments and to explain any details of the project that are not clear to the spectators. More important, you will be questioned by the judges to determine how well you understand the work that you have done.

The project that you are displaying is your own. There is no reason for you to worry that any questions you may be asked will stump you. If the judges should ask you a question to which you do not know the answer, be frank to admit it. You will not be penalized for what you do not know. On the other hand, if you are not well prepared, you may find it difficult to express yourself on a particular point. It is best to try to anticipate some of the questions that may be put to you and to practice your responses to them. Describe the project to your friends. In doing so, you may find concepts that are not clear in your own mind.

If you write a brief synopsis of your entire experiment, it may stand you in good stead when you are asked to explain your project at the fair. If speaking in public is difficult for you, your written notes will offer you a device upon which you can rely.

PART II

Science Fairs

CHAPTER 6

Science Fair Structure

THIS year, well over one million American students will participate in science fairs. Overseas, thousands more will take part in ISF-affiliated fairs. Of these million plus students, approximately four hundred will display their projects at the International Science Fair itself. At the most, two finalists, usually one boy and one girl from your region (the ISF has approximately 240 regional, state, and nationwide affiliates, which send two finalists each), will go on to the International Science Fair.

If you are to be a science fair participant, it is clear that you will be involved with science fairs other than the International Science Fair. Even if you should progress to the ISF, you will have devoted the greater portion of your exhibiting time to other fairs. You should now know something about these other fairs. Where are they? How are they run? You may have many questions about the science fairs below the level of the International Science Fair; it would not be at all surprising if you were confused about these fairs, for science fair structure below the international level is complicated.

You doubtless have heard reference made to local, regional, grade school, junior high, high school, state, and even nationwide science fairs. They all exist, and you might find yourself a participant in any one of them. Not all science fairs are affiliated with the International Science Fair, but most of them are; and a familiarity with the ISF structure is a good beginning for an understanding of the entire organization of science fairs.

To be eligible to display your project at the International Science Fair, you must be a high school student in the tenth, eleventh, or twelfth grade. You must also have won highest honors at an area science fair (regional, state, or nationwide) affiliated with the ISF.

The simplest science fair is the school science fair, be it at grade school, junior high school, or senior high level. If your school has a science fair, you

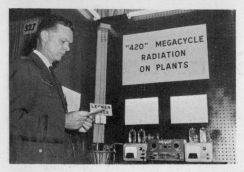

U.S. Air Force

U.S. Air Force

U.S. Air Force

At the ISF, the Air Force selected a winner in each of ten "Aerospace" classifications, including Aerospace Chemistry, Propulsion, Medicine, and Mathematics. Photographs show Air Force judges at work.

Top: Letantia Jankowski, winner in Aerospace Medicine at the 17th ISF, is congratulated by Brigadier General Thomas H. Crouch, Commander, Aerospace Medical Division, Brooks AFB, Texas. (Her project report begins on p. 118.) *Bottom:* Two recent ISF winners were awarded a three-week cruise on the USNS *Sands,* a Navy research and survey ship.

will enter an exhibit there upon completion of a project. If your project is a winner, you might go to a local fair or even to a regional science fair for further competition.

If your school has no science fair, then you will probably exhibit your project first at a local science fair. Such fairs are sponsored by the community, city, or county. The next step would be a regional science fair.

Suppose you won highest honors at your regional science fair. If the fair was an ISF affiliate, you would be sent to the International Science Fair, where judges would compare your project with the top science projects in the nation (and some from other nations). Still another regional fair might be an end in itself, from which the winners retire from competition undefeated. Or if your region was the Greater Boston region of Massachusetts, you would be sent to the Massachusetts State Science Fair instead of to the ISF. In some areas it is the state fair, not the regional, that sends representatives to the International Science Fair. Still another route to the ISF is through the nationwide fair. Nationwide affiliates draw their participants from competitions conducted according to their own specified rules. (Information regarding them is obtainable through Science Clubs of America.)

If you have a project that you feel is a sure winner and you wish to enter ISF competition, you may write to the International Science Fair, 1719 N Street, N.W., Washington, D.C. 20036. For information on the most convenient science fair in your locality, your school advisor or the sponsor of the regional fair in your area would probably be the most helpful. Should you have difficulty in contacting a regional sponsor, ISF again can be of aid.

If you are still in grammar school or junior high, your science fair experience is likely to be parallel with that of a high school student with the one exception that you are not yet eligible to compete on the international level. You will most probably not notice the restriction!

In the chapters that follow, four levels of science fair competition are given close examination. These are the levels through which you may logically progress as you take your first view of science fairs, work at a few projects, broaden your knowledge, and finally take the big step of shooting for the International Science Fair. We will look at science fairs at the grade school, junior high, high school, and regional levels. We will discuss the projects entered, the rules governing the fairs, criteria of judging employed at these fairs, and the types of awards presented.

CHAPTER 7

Grade School Science Fairs

EVEN at the grade school level, science fairs are becoming increasingly widespread. A youngster with only the barest acquaintance with the vast realm of science can become fascinated with an experiment or devote many hours to gathering a collection from nature and displaying it. An interest acquired at this age not infrequently leads to very worthwhile scientific endeavors in later years. The high school student who has been researching his field in ever-increasing portions since grade school has accumulated a formidable background.

The Fairs

Grade school science fairs are, of course, held by the school on the school grounds. Sometimes only one class in the school will have a fair, but usually the entire school will take part. Most often, the winners do not go on to compete in other fairs. Indeed, grade school fairs do not rely on competition to the extent that other science fairs do. Frequently, the science projects are exhibited but not judged. On the other hand, the Kiwanis Regional Science Fair, of Worcester, Massachusetts, displays the outstanding projects from the region's grade schools. In this case, the projects are noncompetitive at the regional level.

Projects

Group projects are common at the grade school level. Because so many grade school science fairs are noncompetitive, and because one of the main

49

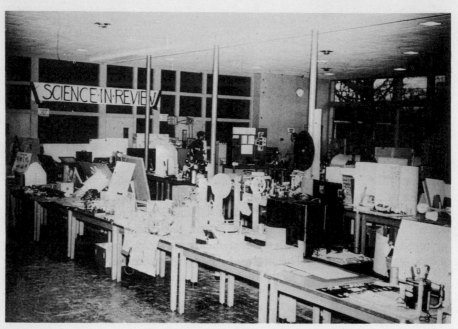

Students' projects on display at a grade school science fair.

goals of science fairs at this level is arousing an active interest in science, such group projects are very suitable.

A project at the grade school level ordinarily deals with the basics of science. Typical projects might include showing how an egg is formed, demonstrating that heat has energy, or observing the different phases of plant growth. You may easily be influenced in your choice of a subject by the area of the country in which you live. In the rural regions of Iowa, animals are frequently the subjects for experimentation and observation. In New York City, on the other hand, grade school students are more likely to study plants because of the difficulty of housing and caring for experimental animals. In the upper grades of the Houston, Texas, schools there is an increased interest in projects related to space research—an outgrowth of

Houston's having become the center of activity for our astronautical endeavors.

The most common grade school projects fall into the "collection, classification, and display" category of science fair projects. If you are in grade school, you might consider collecting and mounting various plants or insects and then classifying them to the best of your ability according to species, genus, order, and family. Your teacher would be glad to help you in this effort. Such a project need not be discontinued after one year; it can be enlarged upon to form the nucleus of a successful junior high or high school project.

Engineering projects are rare at the grade school level, as are theoretical projects. Experimental projects, however, are not at all uncommon. Many experiments are well within the range of abilities of grade school students. A recent winner studied the effects of nicotine from cigarette smoke on goldfish.

Most science fair projects at the grade school level are not accompanied by project notebooks. The projects that *are* well documented, however, are usually the eye-catchers at these fairs. The best advice that can be given to a grade school student interested in preparing a top-flight project for a science fair is to keep a neat, *scientific* record of the progress of his experiment.

Rules

School fairs will vary in their rules, because each school is in complete charge of its own fair. Grade schools, at any rate, have few if any regulations restricting the entry of projects. In general, any project is acceptable even if it is not in actuality a true *science fair project*, one that fits into one of the four categories mentioned above. For example, an illustration, drawn on cardboard, of the human digestive tract, or of the layers of the earth's atmosphere, or of the solar system, although not truly "creative," would be an acceptable exhibit at most grade school science fairs. Participation is valued above all else.

Judging and Awards

In selecting judges, science fairs attempt to strike an equilibrium between the professional and educational worlds. Even at the grade school level, it is not uncommon for a doctor, technician, or scientist to join with teachers in the judging. Science teachers from the local junior high or high school may also help to judge.

In those grade school science fairs where judging of the exhibits takes place, certificates of merit are the highest awards bestowed. The winner receives a special winner's certificate; other noteworthy projects are given runner-up certificates or honorable mentions. As previously noted, competition is not critical in grade school science fairs, but the certificates represent a means of reward for the time and effort the students put into their projects. Often a Certificate of Participation is given to each student exhibitor.

Nearly all these grade school fairs are open for public viewing. Parents, relatives, and friends meet the students and educators, see what is being done as an extracurricular or classroom effort, and, often, the local newspaper will send reporters and photographers to cover the fair.

CHAPTER 8

Junior High School Science Fairs

JUNIOR high school science fairs offer most students their first exposure to any kind of science exhibition. In the junior high fair, the interested participant receives his best preparation for the demanding competition that he will encounter on the high school science fair level. This interest, formed in junior high, will give you the jump on your contemporaries when you reach high school. When one looks at science fairs of this level for their own sake, however, it is obvious that many junior high school projects are excellent.

The Fairs

The junior high science fair, like any school fair, is held on the school grounds. Unlike grade school fairs, however, the junior high winners often advance to regional competition. Many regional fairs structure themselves according to a junior and senior division, the former for junior high school students and the latter for those in senior high. Regions in which science fairs are less strongly supported (a nonprofit regional fair may require a budget of as much as six thousand dollars yearly) either have no junior division at all or else allow junior high school students to participate but do not judge their exhibits.

Projects

Generally speaking, junior high school projects emphasize the practical aspects of our lives; they also lean more toward collection, classification, and display than toward experimentation. Individual and group projects are both popular at this level, and outstanding achievements are common to both. Work in a group if you think that will make you more comfortable, or choose an individual project if you wish.

Projects of all descriptions occur at the junior high school level. You might enter one in botany, medical science, microbiology, psychology, zoology, astronomy, chemistry, biology, earth science, geology, physics, electronics, biochemistry, mathematics, or engineering. Your own science fair will probably not include all these headings, but that is no matter for concern, for many of them overlap. Your project, regardless of the scientific discipline it represents, will find a place at the science fair.

Biology is the most popular field of science for junior high school students. In the New Bedford region of Massachusetts, nearly half the projects exhibited yearly deal with some aspect of biology. Typical topics are studies in heredity or blood typing; environmental studies of microbes; and analyses of the effects of antibiotics on bacteria or vitamins on yeast cultures. Biology projects seem to find particular favor among girls; about half the girls participating in science fairs at the junior high school level submit projects related to the biological sciences.

Physics and electronics are subject areas frequently chosen by junior high school boys. Some project ideas in these fields are: construction of a laser, study of the photoelectric effect, work with modulation of an incandescent light beam, using sound waves as a measure, experimentation with color, the study of heat transfer, or the study of the electrical resistance of certain fluids. Engineering projects appear regularly, but not with the frequency of those in the former two categories. Projects in the theoretical category are almost wholly reserved for the senior high school science fairs.

Psychology experiments are generally popular among junior high school students. At a recent Greater San Diego Regional science fair, a large number of psychology projects appeared. Some titles included: "Does ESP Vary in Youth?", "How Do Sound Waves Affect People?", "Does Color Help People to Remember?", and "Reaction of Goldfish to a Colored Maze."

Science fairs at all levels put a premium on originality or creativity. A simpler, original project is preferred to a more elaborate, nonoriginal project. If you are planning to enter a project at this level, then, the most helpful hint that we can offer you is to move away from the ordinary and so achieve a thought-provoking, creative project, which you can be proud to display at your science fair.

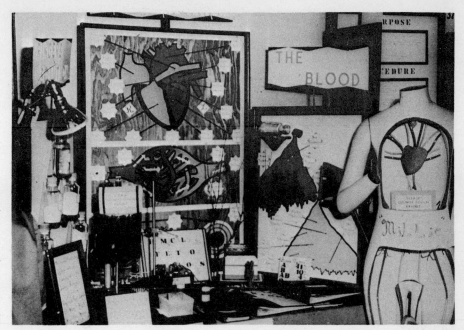

Exhibits such as this one are typical of many submitted by junior high school students. This project would not be acceptable at a science fair at a higher level, since it contains no original experimentation.

Rules

Regulations for junior high school science fairs are most often modeled on the standards of regional fairs and the International Science Fair. Safety warnings must be heeded when you exhibit your project. You have easy access to your school's science fair rules, of course, in the person of your science teacher, who should also be able to advise you concerning any other problems you may have in connection with the fair. Groups enter on the same terms as do individuals, but they compete only against other groups.

In individual competition, boys are matched against boys, and girls against girls, so that in every division one boy and one girl (and perhaps one group) are declared winners, runners-up, and so on.

Judging and Awards

The judging at junior high school science fairs is done primarily by high school science teachers and professional men. Doctors, technicians, scientists, and engineers volunteer their services, and they make conscientious, thorough, and impartial judges. As mentioned previously, they look for originality and creativity above all other qualities. This practice is in keeping with the point system for judging, established by the ISF and included in Part I, Chapter 4. You would do well to review that point table periodically throughout the life of your science fair project.

A certificate of merit or of participation is frequently given to each exhibitor. Other awards presented at this level include: the opportunity for the winners to exhibit their projects at a regional science fair; book awards (science books or dictionaries); and plaques, medals, and so forth. At any science fair level, awards do not play an inordinately large part; but the thrill of winning or simply the excitement of presenting a project representative of your own endeavors is as great at the junior high level as at any other.

CHAPTER 9

High School Science Fairs

YOUR senior high school science fair is the culmination of your science fair experience. At this level appear some very elaborate and well-planned projects; many of them are the result of years of thought and development. The high school fairs highlight the element of competition. Self-satisfaction, the sense of personal accomplishment, remains, however, the greatest single incentive toward repeated science fair participation on the part of the high school student.

The Fairs

Science fairs are more efficiently organized at the high school level than below. The high school fair frequently cooperates directly with the regional fair and, therefore, has the benefit of that larger fair's organizational abilities. Furthermore, since it is larger than either the junior high or the grade school fair, the typical high school fair receives a good deal more publicity. Finally, it might be noted that some school teachers at this level require science fair projects from each student.

Projects

The rules differ from fair to fair on the acceptability of group projects. The International Science Fair does not allow them at all, and many of the

57

regional fairs follow suit. High school is a time to strike out on your own, if you have a topic idea that you feel will lead to a rewarding project.

Projects at the senior high school level are more evenly distributed among the various scientific disciplines than are the junior high science projects. Biology, which, in junior high, is occasionally the subject of 50 percent of all projects is, in high school, "just one other area from which to choose your topic." A chemistry project is as likely as one in biology, and physics, too, accounts for quite a few projects. No science is ignored. At a typical high school science fair you might come across topics ranging from "Effect of Cigarette Smoke on Nuclear Material" to "Can the Honeybee See Color?" to "Salinity Rates along Puget Sound."

While no science holds a clear lead over the others in popularity at high school science fairs, certain areas are more commonly chosen by boys, and others by girls. Physics, for example, remains primarily the domain of boys. Chemistry, on the other hand, is more popular among the girls. Projects such as "Detection of the Aluminum Ion Through Fluorescence," "Distribution of Acids in a Lemon Tree," and "The Identification of Color Additives in Foods" are representative of successful chemistry projects submitted by high school girls.

It is a matter of record at high school science fairs that physics, math, chemistry, engineering, and medicine produce a greater number of *sophisticated* projects than do other areas. Common sense can help to explain why this is so. These areas are generally the most difficult in which to get started; they require a greater degree of basic knowledge; and, often, there is no apparently simple project within these areas. Biology, zoology, botany, or geology, on the other hand, lend themselves to rather easy projects, thus discouraging more demanding undertakings. You might choose to do a simple study of paramecia or snail movement, of the effect of chlorine on plants, or of soil content. But in the same areas you could investigate the effects of radiation upon fetal mice, the seasonal variation of marine life, the hormone regulation of plant growth, or the relationships of rock and soil structures throughout your county. Sophisticated topic ideas may be found in any scientific discipline. In a way, your greatest challenge would be to take one of the so-called "easy" sciences and prove your ability to develop a project of undeniable sophistication.

Senior high projects favor research and experimentation. Engineering projects are common, and a good number of the projects that are not entered in the engineering category demonstrate considerable mechanical skill. At science fairs in Worcester, Massachusetts (a metalworking city, where there are more engineers than scientists), three out of four projects are more nearly engineering than scientific exhibits. Theoretical projects appear for the first time at this level, and collection and display no longer make up most of the students' efforts. The swing is toward creativity and originality, as students like yourself set their sights on the true objectives of science.

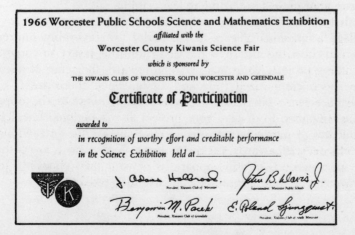

1966 Worcester Public Schools Science and Mathematics Exhibition

affiliated with the

Worcester County Kiwanis Science Fair

which is sponsored by

THE KIWANIS CLUBS OF WORCESTER, SOUTH WORCESTER AND GREENDALE

Certificate of Participation

awarded to
_____

in recognition of worthy effort and creditable performance

in the Science Exhibition held at _____

Top: This girl's project, a winner at her high school science fair, is here shown on display at the regional. *Center:* This high school science fair winner demonstrates the apparatus that he constructed out of odds and ends. *Bottom:* A Certificate of Participation such as this one is often awarded to each science fair exhibitor.

Rules

High school science fair rules are at the discretion of the school, but in most cases remain in accord with regional and ISF rules. Entry is open to the entire top three grades. Boys and girls do not compete with one another; group projects are treated according to locally established rules. Exhibit size is important at the high school fair, because an oversized exhibit, even one of championship caliber, will not be permitted to be displayed at the regional science fair. It is most important to check all the rules thoroughly before entering, lest your hard work be for naught.

Judging and Awards

You will find the judging at your high school science fair to be excellent. Some of the top men in your community will be the judges, men from the academic, medical, and scientific worlds. They will look at your project in every light. Every attempt will be made to be fair and objective, and you can be confident about the merits of the eventual decisions.

The ISF point system, emphasizing creativity, scientific thought, thoroughness, skill, clarity, and dramatic value, will most likely be the basis for the judging. Even if another system is used, however, you can't go wrong if you prepare your project according to ISF criteria.

Rewards for participation in senior high school science fairs are numerous. College admissions officers in particular are favorably impressed by students who show the initiative and dedication necessary to come up with an outstanding project. Your own personal reward, the sense of accomplishment, has been emphasized time and again. Then there are the awards given by the science fair itself. Foremost among these is the opportunity for you, as a winner, to display your project at the regional fair. There are also certificates of participation, special citations for the prizewinners, and book awards or "wish awards" for the winners. Wish awards are cash awards that may be spent on scientific apparatus of your own choosing. In effect, such an award is a grant to continue your scientific research.

CHAPTER 10

Regional Science Fairs

THERE are today over two hundred regional science fairs affiliated with the International Science Fair. Each of these fairs is permitted to send two over-all winners (one boy and one girl) to the annual ISF. The regional fair accepts as many projects from students throughout its locale as it can accommodate. Where exhibition space is ample, all students desiring to exhibit will be permitted to do so. In other circumstances, when there is limited space as well as many applications, it is necessary that the regional fair encourage eliminations at lower levels in order to prevent overcrowding. When this happens, your high school or local science fair will be restricted to sending only a certain number of students to the regional.

The Fairs

Regional fairs may be sponsored by any one of the local organizations; school systems; colleges; academies of science; newspapers; radio and television stations; engineering, medical, or scientific professional societies; industries; or service clubs. A large amount of organization is needed to set up a regional fair; all the work, including procurement of the display hall, printing of programs, plans for the arrangement of exhibits, and so forth, is done on a volunteer basis. Frequently the regional sponsors must involve themselves with the organizational work being done at the school science fairs.

Projects

Exhibited at the regional science fairs are the best of the projects from high school and local science fairs. The competition at the regional level is, therefore, severe. Your project will be up against the best of the projects from each school in your area.

Individual rather than group projects are the core of the regional science fairs. In many cases, group projects may be exhibited, but since these projects are ineligible for International Science Fair competition, a greater amount of excitement centers about the projects being displayed by individuals.

The categories of competition may vary from one regional science fair to another. However, they do, in general, bear some relation to the categories of competition at the ISF level, which are medicine and health, zoology, botany, biochemistry, earth and space sciences, chemistry, physics, and mathematics and computers. Even though your project may not fit into any particular category, it will not necessarily be unacceptable. Many biology projects, for instance, can also be designated medicine or health projects. If not, then the project will in all likelihood fall under the biochemistry designation. A regional fair will make every effort to insure that all projects are treated by the judges with equal scientific regard.

Most regional science fairs are more lenient than the ISF in the matter of categories of competition. Engineering, for instance, is an element essential to many of the best science fair projects, yet it is not now a separate section of the ISF. A section on engineering will be added when and if more engineering projects are entered. At this time, engineering projects are entered in the broader areas of the physical sciences. Many regional science fairs do include engineering, however. The Regional Science Fair of Worcester, Massachusetts treats "engineering" as just one more competitive criterion, and judges *every* project submitted on its engineering merits. At Worcester, a chemistry project utilizing complex apparatus might fail to win a chemistry prize, but instead receive an engineering award for the construction of the apparatus. If you have a project in mind that you fear may not fit well into the categories of competition at the regional level, contact regional science fair authorities and seek their advice. The odds are greatly in your favor that your project will be perfectly acceptable.

The projects exhibited at the regional science fairs are the same as those that were described in the preceeding chapter—the high school science projects. They are, however, the *best* of the high school projects. They are projects that have been developed in a meticulous fashion according to methods described in this book. Names like "Artificial Directional Perception," "Electronic Vowel Synthesis," and "Refraction Index Iodine Value"

Top: Secretary of Labor Willard Wirtz congratulates Ida Jo Rheuark on winning a Labor Department Award at her regional fair. (For her project report, see p. 105.) *Center:* This regional fair is being held in a school gymnasium. *Bottom:* A student explains his project to judges at the all-important regional fair.

do not sufficiently describe the work that was involved in each. In fact, a poor project could have any one of these names. To get an idea of the kind of project it takes to reach the regional, and to win there, you really should see these projects at first hand. If you did so, you could not help but be inspired to greater efforts yourself.

Rules

Regional science fairs attract the foremost men and women in your area for judging. You can be sure that your project will be seen by judges well versed in the area with which it is involved. Yet the burden of convincing the judges of the scientific value of your project remains with you. Assuming that your project meets the criteria of being creative and original, it follows that it represents a new theory or technique for the judge to examine. He must be convinced that your methods were accurate and your findings valid; you must *convince* him of this, as he has no opportunity to run through the project himself and verify your results.

This is not always the most simple task. Virginia Delaney, whose project description is included in Part III, carried her experimentation through to conclusions not supported by prior scientific knowledge. Her project, as first submitted, did not sufficiently convince the judges of the accuracy of her startling find. Only after further experimentation, modification of the presentation, and re-entry of the project the following year, was she able to *prove* what she herself was certain of a year before. The project won a First Award at the International Science Fair.

Regional science fair participation is, of course, a bonus on your college application; achieving distinction at the regional level further enhances your standing before the admissions board. Couple this with the personal satisfaction that you will achieve through competing, and you have more than adequate justification for carrying out your science fair project. There are other rewards at the regional science fairs, such as scholarships; wish awards; encyclopedias; certificates; plaques; and special Army, Navy, Air Force, National Aeronautics and Space Administration, medical, and other awards. Finally, the boy and/or the girl whose projects are judged the best at the regional may be sent, together with their teachers, to the International Science Fair. To display your project at the ISF is the highest privilege of science-fairing—an honor worthy of your greatest efforts. It is also a rare privilege, accorded to few. Set your sights high, but don't be too disappointed if your achievement falls short of your ultimate goal; your work will be its own reward, and no science research project need end when the fair is over. Science is a *never-ending* exploration of the unknown.

PART III

Winning Projects

1. Analyzing some Relationships in Prime Modular Arithmetic

By Priscilla Chow

I first began this project as a freshman in high school, working with subtraction and division in prime number modulos (mods), the construction of tables showing these results, and the possibility of writing equations that could produce the results directly.

In the following year, I attempted to make a linear slide rule for the numbers in Mod 7. I was unsuccessful in this, and then directed my efforts towards a circular form of slide rule, since this was a circular arithmetic. I was successful in this and in the process also discovered how a linear slide rule could be constructed. At the 14th NSF-I (now known as ISF) a professor told me how I could use base 3, raise it to 6 successive integral powers, convert the results to Mod 7, and thus obtain a simpler slide rule. I then tried to determine why this was so, and through trial and error was able to arrive at the lowest possible integral base and set it generates. This enabled me to produce a workable slide rule scale for that mod. A workable set contained M-1 numbers from 1 to M-1 in a specific order, where M was the natural number on which the mod was based. But I was not very successful in answering the why of my questions. Moreover, the methods I used were not simple, and they required a great deal of time and paperwork. It occurred to me that perhaps I was going about it in the wrong way, and so I decided to analyze results which I had previously set aside. Why were these numbers in a certain order? Could there be another order for these numbers, and could I still get a workable set for a slide rule? Why did certain numbers keep appearing in the non-workable bases? What kind of numbers will form a workable base?

I first made tables for each prime number mod from 2 to 79, listing each base and the set generated from 2 to the M-1 base. With this done, I raised more questions, but was also able to get some answers. I could see which bases produced a workable set and which ones did not. I could see that the last number in each base was always 1, and after that the set would repeat itself in the same order. Also, any Set A, Mod M, would be an ordered set of natural numbers and the number just before the 1 in that set would produce the same set of positive integers as Set A, Mod M, but in the reverse order.

This worked in every case. Further, the product of each first number in Set A and each penultimate number in that set was always congruent to 1, Mod M; and also the product of each second number and each third-to-the-last number is congruent to 1, Mod M, and so on. I then decided that there must be some relationship among these numbers. By means of graphs, I determined that the natural squares were never a workable base. I also discovered from my tables that for any mod, the M-1 base would always have

Priscilla Chow won a Second Award at the 16th ISF for her theoretical project.

two numbers, M-1 and 1. Why? I found that, algebraically, when the number M-1 is squared and converted to that mod, the only term without an M variable is the number 1, which is the remainder and the answer in modular arithmetic.

By taking a more careful look at my tables, I saw that every other number starting with the second number in the set would never be a working base for that mod. Moreover, not all of the remaining numbers would be a workable base for that mod. Again, if M-1 contained the factor 2 and some other prime number as a factor, then there would be $\dfrac{M-3}{2}$ workable bases and the same number of non-workable bases, plus the M-1 base, which would have just two numbers. Also, the count of the numbers in the non-working bases would be that prime number which M-1 contained as a factor. However, if M-1 was factorable by 2 as well as some non-prime number, the count of the numbers in the non-workable base would be that number which was the factor other than 2. I have not yet found out how many workable bases, nor how many non-workable bases, exist in Mod M.

Since the order of the numbers seemed to follow a special law of formation, there may be something significant in the differences of each workable and nonworkable set. At least I have found that they form an interesting pattern.

Another point which I considered was the occurrence of each number of one workable set in relationship to any other workable set in that same mod. I found a pattern in which all of the workable bases were produced, and another in which just half of them were produced. To get the remaining half I found that it was necessary to reverse each set. I also found that I could obtain a non-working set from a working set. Why this is so is still an unanswered question for me.

In summary, although I have not reached any definite conclusions as to how modular arithmetic operates, I have acquired a better insight into the workings of number systems in general.

At present, I do not know of any practical use for the relationships I have found, but this was not the primary reason for the research I have conducted. My principal reason was to explore number systems, a field about which I knew very little before I started my work.

WHY DID I DO A MATHEMATICS PROJECT? ALSO, WHAT DOES IT COST TO DO THIS TYPE OF PROJECT?

Since I am from a large family, it was not possible to have even a modest amount of laboratory equipment around the home. This meant eliminating the study of animal behavior or even plant behavior. Physics and Chemistry also required gadgets and equipment which I could not afford. Moreover,

Mathematics was my particular field of interest, and research in this field could be done with paper and pencil at home, at school, while waiting for the bus, baby-sitting, and in many other places. For me, the mathematical project had decided advantages.

The money I spent on my project was confined to materials for my displays exhibited at the school and International Science Fairs. The total cost of material for this last fair was about twenty dollars.

How Did I Become Interested in This Research?

To become eligible for membership in the Hawaiian Junior Academy of Science, it is necessary to submit a paper covering either a research project or an experiment. At the suggestion of my mathematics teacher, I started what turned out to be four years of intensive work on the Modulo System. My class had just finished learning how to add and multiply in mods. I decided to investigate subtraction and division. First I displayed results in tabular form. Then I tried to write equations which would give results directly. This led to my second project ("A Slide Rule for Modulo 7"), and also a third ("Logarithms and Modulos") in which I used the base concept to generate a workable set. However, there was no easy method or pattern for determining the numbers needed for the slide rule scales. I then decided to examine what I had obtained thus far in tabular form. "Analyzing Some Relationships in Prime Modular Arithmetic" became my fourth project.

2. The Physiological and Behavioral Effects upon the Cardiovascular and Musculoskeletal Systems of the White Rodent, as induced by Simulated Space Flight

By John L. Gilkey

INTRODUCTION: Since I have been working in the field of Bioastronautics for the past five years, there was little difficulty in selecting a project. I have done some preliminary work with rocket sleds and a home-made centrifuge. After my work with earth-based equipment, I decided to do flight testing. PROBLEM: My problem was to determine what effect, if any, long-term subjection to a space environment would have upon the circulatory, muscle, and skeletal systems. I was also faced with the problem of designing test equipment capable of simulating an environment equivalent to that of space. PROCEDURE: My project was divided into four major divisions. They were #1: EXTREME GRAVITY TESTS, #2: WATER IMMERSION TESTS, #3: ROCKET TESTS, and #4: ZERO GRAVITY FLIGHT PARABOLAS.

The extreme gravity tests were the first phase of my experimentation. These tests were conducted with the aid of a multi-axis rotating device, which was used to simulate rapid yaw, pitch, and roll. In order to derive useful information from these tests, it was necessary to use a radiotelemetry unit to radio back the heart rate of the mouse during the test. Ten mice were used in this phase, with each mouse undergoing one each of the yaw, pitch, and roll tests. Each mouse was strapped into a foam couch at the center of the rotating table, and was rotated at the following speeds: YAW—300 rpm, PITCH—100 rpm, ROLL—150 rpm.

In the second phase of my experiment, I designed and constructed a water-immersion tank for the purpose of studying the effects of a 10-day subjection period to zero gravity. In this test, 3 mice were immersed vertically, up to the neck, in a tank of water. EKG electrodes were attached, and readouts were taken before and after the 10-day period. After the test, the mice were X-rayed to determine the extent of osteoporosis. Then arteriograms were made to study dilation of the circulatory systems. Finally, the mice were dissected, and tissue slides were made of the heart, spleen, liver, kidney, and the external jugular vein. From those slides, photomicrographs were made for close examination.

The third phase of my experiment entailed the design and construction of a solid fuel rocket capable of lifting a mouse, radiotelemetry system, and a parachute recovery system, to an altitude of 2,000 feet. The booster used was one which I had designed several years earlier and which could be adapted to this purpose.

The mouse was placed in the capsule along with the radio transmitter. The capsule was then mounted onto the rocket by means of an insert plug. Separation was achieved by an acid-chemical switch: A pellet of potassium

71

Rocket No.   1
Name or Model No.   1

FIRING DATA SHEET

PLACE: New Albany, Ind.   DATE: 24 Mar. 66   TIME: 4:30

WEATHER DATA: ROCKET DATA:

TEMPERATURE	58		NAME	R - 1
WIND DIRECTION	W		LENGTH	83"
WIND VELOCITY	4 mph		O.D.	2 1/8
PRECIPITATION	0		NO. FINS 4	TYPE D. Sq.
VISIBILITY	Unl.		WEIGHT EMPTY	8.2 lbs
CEILING	Unl.		WEIGHT LOADED	17.7 lbs
HUMIDITY	21%			

PROPELLANT DATA: NOZZLE DATA:

TYPE	Zn & S		TYPE	DeLavale
MIXTURE	2.04/1 Zn/S		LENGTH	4.06"
WEIGHT	9.5 lbs.		THROAT AREA	.682 sq. in
DENSITY	.059 lbs/c. in		EXIT AREA	5.59 sq. in
BURNING RATE	90 in./sec		O.D.	2.0 in
SPEC. IMP.	35		MATERIAL	CRS

EXPECTED PERFORMANCE: COMBUSTION CHAMBER:

			CROSS. AREA	75.36 c. in
TOTAL THRUST	800 lbs		LENGTH	24 in.
BURNING TIME	.5 sec.		WALL THICK.	1/16 in.
EXHAUST VEL.	1500 ft/sec		MATERIAL	SAE 1020 St.

LAUNCHING DATA: INSTURMENTATION & SPECIAL DATA:

LAUNCHER USED	Rod	Rocket carried mouse and
LAUNCHING ANGLE	80	radio transmitter
DIRECTION	183	

REMARKS:

    Good flight pattern.

Top: John Gilkey's project in the field of Bioastronautics, which studied the reactions of mice to extreme gravity and weightlessness, received a Second Award at the 17th ISF. *Bottom:* Firing Data Sheet used by John Gilkey in the rocket-testing phase of his study.

chloride and sugar was placed above a glass cylinder containing sulphuric acid. As the rocket tipped over at peak-trajectory, the acid made contact with the pellet, thus igniting it, which in turn ignited a black-powder charge. The rocket was fired twice, each time carrying one mouse.

The fourth and final phase of my project was the study of short-term full weightlessness. This time the zero gravity effect was produced by flying through a Keplerian Trajectory in a Cessna 172. During the trajectory, heart rates of the 3 mice were recorded, and motion pictures were taken to study disorientation.

RESULTS:

EXTREME GRAVITY TESTS: The results of this phase of the experiment show up very dramatically in the test evaluation sheets I compiled for this portion of my work. As I had expected, heart rates increased very rapidly during the first few seconds of extreme gravity. This can be attributed to the sudden overload placed on the heart in so far as the weight of the blood is concerned. This excessive rate soon began to diminish at a fairly constant rate until it reached a point just above normal. This point corresponds with the strain placed on the heart by the sustained motion of the rotating table.

The increase was most severe in the yaw simulation at 300 revolutions per minute. In these tests, the rates increased to 905 beats per minute before beginning to diminish.

In the pitch simulation, heart rates increased shortly to a point of 795, then began to decrease, eventually reaching a rate of 10 beats per minute slower than normal.

Roll simulation had a very similar effect upon the mice to that of the yaw tests. Rates increased to 900 beats per minute, then began to subside.

WATER IMMERSION TESTS: Heart rates, as I had expected, dropped from their normal of 780 to 550 after only 48 hours in the water immersion tank. These rates remained about the same throughout the remainder of the test period, fluctuating only plus or minus 8 beats per minute.

After removal from the tank, the bone density X rays were taken. They showed that very little, if any, osteoporosis had taken place in any of the major bones that I had compared: femur, tibis, humerus, and caudal vertebrae.

Arteriograms showed extreme dilation of the inferior vena cava in all of the test mice. Dilation was in the area of 1 to 1.5 millimeters. Arterial dilation was less severe, being in the range of .50 to .75 millimeters. This was noted by measuring the size of the aorta.

Cross-sectional slides of the heart, spleen, left kidney, median lobe of the liver, and external jugular vein show, very profusely, the dilation of the different veins and arteries throughout the anatomy of the mouse.

There was no loss in over-all length of the mice, and loss in weight for any one mouse did not exceed 0.25 grams. Hearts in the experimental group were generally smaller than in the control group. Weight differences were on the average of 0.045 grams, in comparison to a heart weight of 0.180 grams.

ROCKET TESTS: The heart rate of the mouse increased to about 800 beats per minute immediately after coming out of the influence of the ether. During the pre-launch period, there was a gradual decrease in heart rate as the mouse became accustomed to its surroundings.

The first peak in heart rate came at the moment of ignition. There was no thrust at this time but there was the sound of the propellant grain as it began to burn. Rates rose only slightly at this point—to 795 beats per minute.

The second major peak came at the moment of lift-off. Heart rates rose very rapidly to 925 beats per minute, and held this rate for the powered portion of the flight. Accelerometer readings indicate a G level of 30 G's. After booster engine cut-off, the mice underwent a period of deceleration. Over a 7-second period, the mice dropped from a 30 G load to a zero gravity state. During this period, heart rates decreased to 910 beats per minute.

As the rocket reached peak trajectory and began pitch-over (this is the zero gravity portion of the flight), heart rates again increased to 920 beats per minute.

After separation, the heart rates slowly began diminishing to normal. At approximately 30 seconds into the flight, the heart rate then returned to normal.

SHORT-TERM ZERO GRAVITY: Gravity posed no severe problems. Heart rates did increase approximately +50 beats per minute, but returned to normal very shortly after the test. There was extensive disorientation when the mice were flown through the trajectory without any reference platform, but when the platform was present, no disorientation was noticeable.

CONCLUSIONS: Reactions to weightlessness and extreme gravity have been considered as possible limiting factors in the exploration of space. The body systems that are most frequently represented as potential problems are the cardiovascular and musculoskeletal. Most of the mice tested exhibited an increase in heart rate upon returning to a 1 G environment. This condition, called orthostatic hypotension, often results in fainting, thus indicating a temporary collapse of the circulatory system.

This collapse of the circulatory system may not be quite as serious as it seems. Although there was extensive dilation of the cardiovascular system under zero gravity conditions, fainting did not occur in any of the mice that I tested with, nor did it occur during any of the extreme gravity tests. This tends to indicate that although orthostatic hypotension occurs due to subjection to the conditions, its presence is to no drastic degree.

Should the mice, however, be subjected to an extreme G load immediately after long-term weightlessness, fainting would more than likely occur, due to too great an overload being placed upon the heart. It would be possible, however, to reduce the likelihood of fainting, by increasing the inter-cardiovascular pressure during the time spent in zero G.

EXTREME GRAVITY SIMULATOR

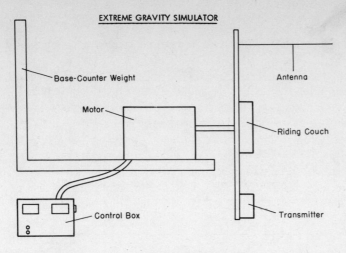

Base-Counter Weight

Antenna

Motor

Riding Couch

Control Box

Transmitter

WATER IMMERSION RACK

Terminal Bar

EKG Leads

EKG Electrode

Hinge

Mouse

EKG Electrode

Tape

ROCKET CAPSULE

Antenna (30")

Air Intakes

Transmitter

9v Battery

Breathing Chamber

Microphone

Capsule Material - SAE 1020 Stl. Tb.

Over-All Length - 45"

Diameter - 2⅛"

Parachute

Testing equipment above was designed and built by John Gilkey to simulate environmental conditions of space.

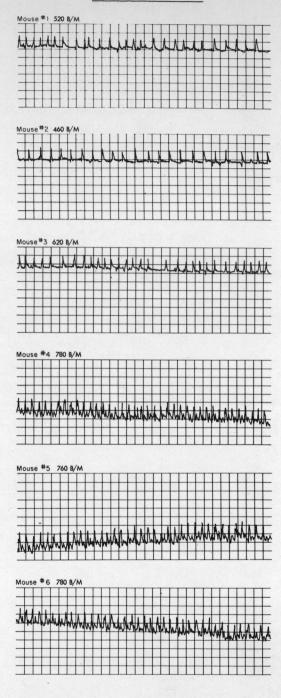

Electrocardiograms recorded changes in heart rates over a ten-day subjection to zero gravity.

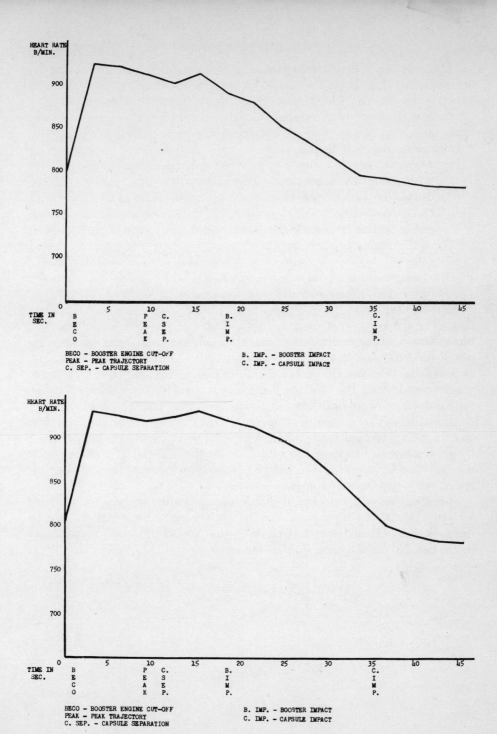

Moment-to-moment changes in heart rate during the rocket tests may be seen on these Heart Rate/Time graphs for two of the mice.

This could be accomplished by merely increasing the pressure outside the organism. All that would be required would be to wear an elastic suit, increasing the external pressure and inhibiting the flow of the blood.

Space flight for a long duration of time seems to pose no severe problems, since man can regulate his exercise and external body pressure.

I therefore conclude the following:

(1) Man can survive extreme gravity for a short period of time without undergoing any severe physical damage.

(2) Subjection to a zero gravity environment for a prolonged period of time has a definite dilative effect upon the cardiovascular system; however, this orthostatic hypotension does not cause fainting so long as the organism is returned to a normal 1 G environment at a gradual rate.

(3) Osteoporosis does not occur to any measurable degree so long as the organism is exercised for at least 15 minutes daily.

EXPENDITURES on my project were surprisingly low, when one considers that all of the equipment used was valued at several hundred dollars. The rocket was built for under $20.00, and the fuel cost only about $10.00. The use of the EKG machine was free, along with the X-ray machine. The cost of the tissue slides was the cost of the slides themselves, and the photomicrographs cost $20.00. The airplane flight was about $10.00 an hour. All other test instruments were built from materials found around the home.

Approximately one year was spent on the project, with the first five months being devoted entirely to research in the field. After this period, I began work with design and construction of the equipment that I was to use. Invaluable help was received from a number of local doctors who allowed me to use their equipment.

There was very little technical data available in my field, although there was an abundance of generalized material. Technical data in reference to the rocket that I used was derived from the *Rocket Manual for Amateurs* by Brinley. No other technical reports were used.

3. *Abnormal Pregnancies in the Lebistes reticulatus*

By Virginia L. Delaney

As a freshman in high school, I was privileged to have an enthusiastic biology teacher who insisted that each of his students create a science project in some field of the broad category of science. The only requirement was that the topic we chose was to be of interest to us. In early January I began reading articles, which I hoped would give me an idea for a project. Among my readings I included magazines and books of science projects, the suggestions for "further study" in our text, and scientific journals. In one reference I found mentioned the interesting fact that female guppies separated from the male for long periods of time have often given birth to litters of fry. Although time did not allow me to explore the topic for that fair, my curiosity was so aroused that I began to collect information and to plan a project which lasted over four years, and in fact still continues today.

In exploring the literature in the public libraries (I used the libraries of neighboring colleges too), I found much information about the guppy (*Lebistes reticulatus*). It is a small tropical fish, which varies in size at maturity from half an inch to an inch. The male is brilliantly colored while the larger female is tan, gold, or gray, depending upon the variety. At birth the fry are about an eighth of an inch long, and sex determination while possible is not accurate. However, breeding does not occur until two weeks after the male gonopodium develops. Litters are frequent; the gestation period is twenty-eight days, and the number of fry born may vary from three to sixty. The average size in my tanks was ten to fifteen.

By June I was ready to begin experimentation. *The Index of Periodical Literature* had made available a few articles about guppy reproduction, and the references in these articles had led me to others of particular interest. The journals I wanted were usually available to me in either my town library, local college libraries, or the library in a nearby city. I wrote to a scientist in India for a reprint of one article that I was unable to locate, and *Science News Letter* sent me a copy of one of their old editions, which contained an article of interest. From these references I found that there were four major theories. The most prominent one was that the female stored sperm cells from one insemination, later fertilizing from five to eight litters with the stored semen. A more recent theory suggested that the male secreted a chemical (possibly sperms) into the water, which caused pregnancies even after the male had been removed. Evidence also indicated that either hermaphroditism (bisexualism) or parthenogenesis (the development of an egg cell without a sperm) could cause the observed births.

I planned experiments which would exclude the most improbable theories or would indicate that one of the other theories was probably correct. We had some of the equipment I needed in our basement—an old tank, filter, net, and siphon. I visited pet shop sales, closeouts, and discount

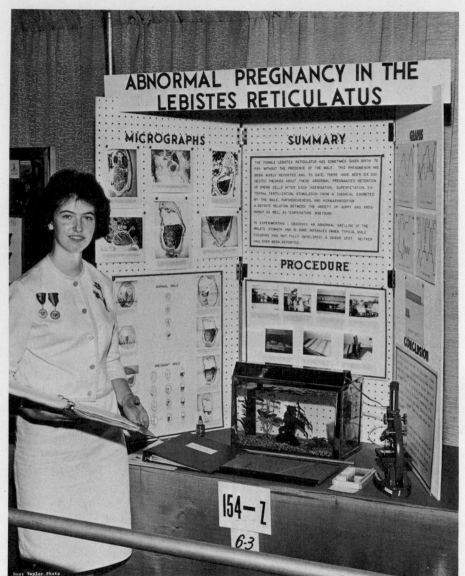

Since Virginia Delaney's study of parthenogenesis and hermaphroditism in the guppy arrived at conclusions not supported by prior scientific knowledge, ISF judges were not convinced of the accuracy of her findings. After additional experimentation, she re-entered the project at the 16th ISF the following year, when it won a First Award.

sales, slowly adding to my equipment over the four-year period. For one birthday I received a used pump, two stands, and another tank. Money I won in awards was also used to buy equipment such as a microscope. Guppies themselves weren't expensive, and once I began I found that few fish had to be bought.

In my first experiments I found that virgin females as well as those who had previously been bred were capable of these "abnormal pregnancies." Thus my science fair project presented in 1963 dealt with the inability of the theory that the female guppy stored sperm cells to explain the observations. While it was still possible that the fish did, it was apparent from my work that not every female stored the semen for later use. In fact only one particular variety—the "wild variety" (characterized by a dark pigmentation around its scales)—was observed to reproduce after separation from the male. Other reports indicated that other varieties of guppies had in the past reproduced without a male. It then became evident that these fish of the same variety possessed this common ability because they were interrelated and had inherited the ability.

In the next year I found that virgin females in tap water also exhibited signs of pregnancy, an enlarged stomach and dark gravid spot. At the stage of pregnancy, near the end of the twenty-eight-day gestation period, the stomach begins to fill out, and finally the swelling extends from beneath the gills to the gravid spot. The gravid spot in the guppy is found just above the anus. It is a round area of pigmentation which darkens in color as a result of a high concentration of the pigment melanin. In the non-pregnant guppy, or in early pregnancy, the spot is light tan in color. Near the end of pregnancy the pigmentation is so pronounced that the area appears dark brown or even black. It is thus possible to determine by external observation the approximate stage of pregnancy.

While external observation of many virgin females indicated that the fish were in early or even middle stages of pregnancy, few births occurred. In total only twenty-seven fry were born. These litters were small and the mortality rate was high. Within the first twelve hours after birth, thirty-six percent of these fish died, while the mortality rate in normal births was eight percent in the first twenty-four hours in my tanks.

In 1964 I presented my second science fair project on these abnormal births at the National Science Fair International. I had to this point found that the theory concerning insemination through the water of the aquarium by an absent male was not a possibility. Rather, the observed pregnancies were a result of some inherited factor passed from one generation to another in my strain of guppy. Either parthenogenesis or hermaphroditism could cause the observed births, but without histological study I could not determine which was responsible. The equipment I needed for this phase of my project seemed to be out of reach. I wrote to hospitals, laboratories, and even the Army Research Unit in a neighboring town. Finally what appeared

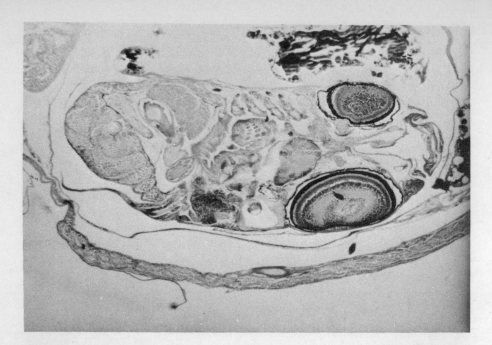

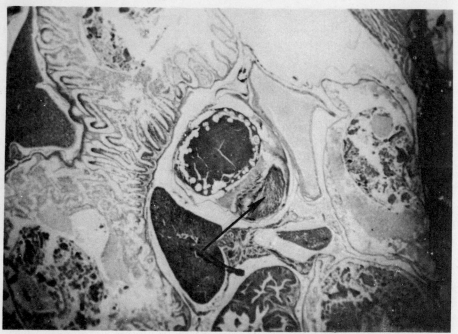

Photomicrographs on these two pages suggest some of the remarkable findings of Virginia Delaney's study. *Top:* An embryo in a normal pregnant female nearing the end of the gestation period. Dark, ovoid areas are the embryo's eyes. At the top are the remains of the yolk sac. *Bottom:* An embryo (indicated by arrow) in a normal pregnant female. Note the yolk sac beneath the embryo.

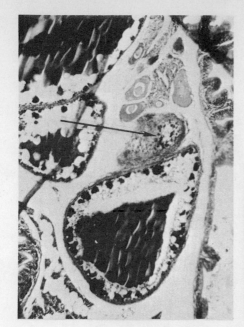

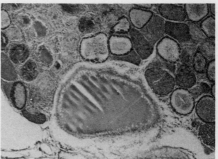

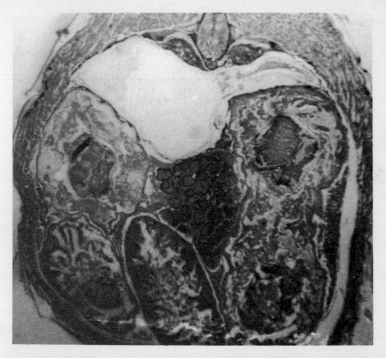

Left: An embryo (indicated by arrow) in a normal pregnant female. Beneath it is the yolk sac; above it are several egg cells in different stages of development. *Top, right:* Testis and egg cell in the hermaphroditic male. No embryo is present. *Bottom:* Around testis the (triangular dark area) of a normal male, two melanin-lined sacs are apparent.

to be an insurmountable obstacle was overcome. My hopes had been heightened when I was chosen to work at the Army unit on a research project, but to my dismay I found they did not have the equipment I would need. When I explained my deep disappointment to one of my friends, she remarked that maybe her mother, a doctor, might be able to help. That afternoon, Dr. Lorna D. Johnson agreed to allow me to use her laboratory, and her technician, Miss Nancy Koster, later showed me the techniques I needed to complete my project. To both of them and Dr. Johnson's daughter I owe my deepest gratitude.

After mastering the techniques I sectioned virgin female guppies that were apparently pregnant, as well as normal pregnant females, normal females, and normal males. When I examined the slides of the virgin females, some showed developing egg cells. In one instance a recognizable cross section of an embryo is apparent. No distinct testis or "ovotestis," an area consisting both of ovarian and testicular tissue, was found in these fish. Thus it is evident that the observed births are a result of the development of an unfertilized egg cell in one strain of the guppy. The tendency toward parthenogenesis is inherited thus appearing in only one strain of my fish. While parthenogenesis often appears in lower animals, the unfertilized egg seldom reaches the final stages of development. Without the stimulus of the sperm cell, the egg's development is stunted and disintegrates. Those eggs that do continue to develop have only one set of twenty-three chromosomes (the same number that man receives from each parent). In these resulting fish, the high mortality rate is probably due to its chromosomal insufficiency. While the fish may function normally in all aspects except reproduction, the effect of any defective genes cannot be repressed by a normal homologous chromosome. Thus a normally recessive lethal gene would be dominant in these fish, which have only one set of chromosomes. They are more susceptible to the damaging effects of genetic diseases, and few live to maturity.

While my project was directly concerned only with the reproduction of the female, in breeding fish I found that in some of the males the stomach appeared to be swollen. The swelling was erratic; it did not appear at evenly spaced intervals. These males, like the females, were larger in size than the normal males. To illustrate, using the microtome I made serial sections of these fish as well as normal males. The testis of the normal male appeared in forty-five serial sections, while that of these males appeared in one hundred and fifteen, or 2.6 times as many.

I was able to identify ovarian tissue in these males, and in one instance what appeared to be an egg cell is apparent. I treated normal females with an overdose of methyltestosterone, a male hormone, to determine its effect upon their reproduction. It soon became apparent that the opening through which the fry is extruded gradually shrank in size until the fry were alternately stuck, or unable to pass through. Thus even if these hermaphroditic males were capable of self-fertilization, births could not occur.

There are many aspects of this project which are still incomplete, and in which I hope someday to be able to continue my research. Perhaps the role of melanin, a dark pigment, is the most interesting. In the normal male, two "sacs" surround the testis. These melanin-lined sacs have no known purpose and to my knowledge had never before been observed. Melanin seems to play a widespread role in the female and male. But what controls the melanin concentration in particular portions of the fish both internally and externally? Could it be the pineal body, a little-understood gland, which in chameleons regulates color changes? So much remains to be done, but time does not permit all that I wish to do. A science project may be very costly in respect to time, yet it is well worth it. Despite the many hours I spent weekly on my project, I've never felt it interfered with my other activities, and the benefits far exceed the costs.

4. Can Ultrasonic Sound Kill Bacteria?

By Frederick Dana Hess

Choosing my topic was my easiest task. While reading a physics assignment, I noted that ultrasonic sound had been used to kill bacteria. This was all that was necessary to start a project on a life span which concluded at the International Science Fair in St. Louis, Missouri.

My first step after choosing the topic was to learn as much about it as I could. There was a world of information at my fingertips, including my home town library and the Washington State University library and Department of Bacteriology.

At the local library I read material on ultrasonic sound and bacteria, but nothing was available on the two combined. A great help was the science library at Washington State University, where I obtained my first information on ultrasonic cavitation of bacteria. The next step was a letter to Washington State University's Department of Bacteriology requesting specific information on bacteria and their ultrasonic destruction. Again I drew a blank on the effect of ultrasonic sound on bacteria, but I did gain a great deal of information on bacteria from the department. A textbook on bacteria-handling techniques (*Microbiology*, by Pelczar and Reid) was particularly helpful, inasmuch as I had never before handled bacteria. I also obtained agreement for them to send me cultures of bacteria when I had made sufficient preparation for them.

It was suggested to me by a teacher to write the Department of Commerce in Washington, D.C., and request a bibliography on the effects of ultrasonic sound on bacteria. After receiving the bibliography, I requested a reprint of a Russian research paper that dealt with this subject. This reprint was of much value and gave me a basis upon which to start my project.

A person should not be afraid to write to anyone asking for information. I wrote Walt Disney Studios requesting information on cartoon characters I planned to use on my project, and received an answer from them. This shows that everyone is interested in education.

One of my most important information resources was Washington State University. I spent many hours in the library and talking to the professors. Every professor I talked to was very willing to give me any information I asked for. After telling them what I was doing, I was never rejected. Permission was even granted for me to use the electron microscope to view experimentation results at a high magnification, and I was privileged to photograph those results.

The most important part of any successful science project is the research done in the form of experimentation. I feel a science project deals with research that has not been previously done. My experimentation was the basis for my entire project. I picked out one problem which was, "Can Ultrasonic Sound Kill Bacteria?", and made variations of that problem.

Frederick D. Hess exposed bacterial cultures to ultrasonic sound. His project received a Second Award at the 16th ISF.

Using only two different types of bacteria permitted a thorough job on each type. I submitted the bacteria to four different time exposures of the ultrasonic sound, which ranged from one to thirty minutes. Each exposure was repeated many times to assure accuracy on the percent of kill. Each experiment was carried out with much care, and I was very careful in recording the results. The bulk of the time spent on my project was on this experimentation.

One of the most interesting parts of my project was the construction of the apparatus used for experimentation and display. Everything on my project was handmade—from an incubator to keep the bacteria at a desired temperature to an oscillator used to drive the transducer unit that produced the ultrasonic waves.

Only twice was I required to obtain assistance: once when the electron microscope was used to photograph the bacteria, and once when a friend of mine helped me with the cartoon characters that were used with my project.

Science projects are not without problems and setbacks, and my project was no exception. One morning I looked in my incubator and saw that all my previous day's experiments were contaminated, as well as the pure cultures of bacteria which were used during the experiments to obtain samples. Being able to find two small cultures that were not affected, I transferred them to sterile media. Then I sterilized everything that was used for experimentation and started over again. The problem was overcome by this method without much difficulty. It seems that endurance is a part of every science project.

Parents' favorite complaint about science projects is the expense they require. Money must be spent, but if caution is used it can be kept to a minimum. People estimated that my project cost approximately $400, but it actually cost $125. Take a tip from me and borrow as many items as possible. Parts can be obtained free if you tell the company what you are using them for. I received all the glass and wood used in the incubator free from the local lumber company by explaining to them that it was to be used in a science project. A cost of $125 sounds outrageous, but an all-expense-paid trip for one week from Quincy, Washington, to St. Louis, Missouri, is valued at much more than $125. Also one must not forget the priceless personal rewards gained in experiences while working with science projects.

In presentation of a project, a person cannot be afraid to try something a little different. I used a short cartoon sketch to introduce my project, and it was received quite well. A large amount of color was used on my posters and the writing was kept to a minimum. All detailed information was presented in a 42-page comprehensive report, which accompanied my project. Most important in presenting a project is neatness and clarity.

I was once told that to win awards in high school one must be an athlete.

I proved them wrong by winning four grand awards at our High School Science Fair; a first, fourth, and grand award at the District Science Fair; and a second-place award at National Science Fair International.

In four years of high school I received seven ribbons, four trophies, and eight medals, along with many memories I wouldn't trade for anything. I could spend hours thinking about the places I went, the awards I received, and the people I met, all due to science fair projects that everyone seems to dread so much.

5. Amminization of Transition Metal Sulfates

By Carolyn C. Gerhardt

Ammonia complexes, or ammines, are complexes readily formed by some transition metals. Several years ago I became interested in these complexes through reading and did some preliminary work with them. This year I worked only with the sulfate ammines, attempted to perform some analysis of those prepared, and used a new method for precipitation of the ammine salts.

The first step in developing a chemical synthesis project such as this one is a thorough researching of the topic of transition metal complexes in general and ammines in particular. Using the facilities of both my high school library and Jacksonville University, I studied complexes, their theory and preparation. This research took approximately two months, but also continued throughout my project.

The general method of ammine production is the addition of ammonia to the metal salt dissolved in a minimum of water. Initial addition of ammonia aqueous precipitates the metal hydroxide, which then dissolves in an excess of ammonia to form the complex ammine. In the case of chromium ammines, heat is applied to facilitate production. I used this general procedure to form four ammine sulfates—with copper, nickel, zinc, and chromium. By researching the *Chemical Abstracts* (1907–1965), I verified that the tetraammine zinc (II) sulfate and the hexaammine chromium (III) sulfate were original, in that their preparation had not previously been reported.

Once I formed the ammines, I divided them into two samples and treated them in the following ways:

1. I added absolute alcohol directly to the solution to precipitate the ammine sulfate. This worked with all four ammines.

2. I placed the second sample in a desiccator (KOH) with absolute ethanol in another beaker placed next to the ammine solution. A saturated ammonia atmosphere was employed to control efflorescent decomposition. The alcohol diffused across to the ammine, precipitating large, well-formed, needle-like crystals. Nickel, copper, and chromium ammine sulfates were precipitated by this method. Previously its use had been reported only for copper ammine sulfate.

The solid ammine salts were necessary for analysis of the product. The second method yielded purer and larger crystals than the first.

I now faced the problem of verification of my complexes. Having worked with the techniques of titration and thermogravimetry in two National Science Foundation Institutes, I decided to use these methods for analysis.

Thermal decomposition was accomplished by heating the crystals in an oven at 150 degrees C. and recording the weight change until a constant

In her chemical synthesis project, which received a First Award at the 17th ISF, Carolyn Gerhardt prepared the ammine sulfates for four transition metals.

weight was reached. Ammines decomposed in discrete amounts at specific temperatures, releasing ammonia. By comparing the theoretical weight loss with the actual one, the original molecular formulae can be verified. I analyzed the copper, nickel, and chromium ammines by this method. In all cases, the formulae were verified. In the case of copper the loss corresponded to two moles of ammonia and one mole of water; with nickel, to two moles of ammonia; with chromium, to eight moles of ammonia.

I then titrated crystals of the copper and chromium ammines against HCl with a methyl orange indicator. By calculation I determined the gram equivalents per milliliter in the ammonia and compared against the theoretical yield. This also verified my results.

Finally I established the presence of sulfate in all my complexes by a qualitative precipitation using barium chloride.

Thus, I prepared two classical and two original transition metal ammine sulfates. The formulae were:

1. $[Cu(NH_3)4H_2O]SO4$
2. $[Ni(NH_3)6]SO4$
3. $[Zn(NH_3)4]SO4$
4. $[Cr(NH_3)6]2(SO4)_3$

My project work lasted about eight months. Throughout this time I kept a laboratory notebook, recording my daily work and research. All experimentation was done before and after school in my high school laboratory. My expenses were small, as I was able to use the school's equipment and chemicals. I paid about ten dollars for those chemicals I used in quantity.

Ammines are most useful in terms of chemical analysis. They may dissolve or prevent precipitation, separate compounds, or analyze certain elements by homogeneous catalysts and in the purification of water.

6. *Algae, Man, and the Future*

By Gregory G. Marchand

My study resulted from a curiosity about something which annoyed me. While swimming in lakes and ponds, I noticed a thick mass of slimy substance covering the surface of the water and coated on logs and rocks beneath the water. It seemed a very unpleasant thing with which to come in contact. I took some of the material to school to find what it was.

Upon discovering that it was a plant commonly known as "pond scum" or "algae," I obtained books from the library about it and began looking through them. I found that not only was this plant a nuisance to me, but that many other people were bothered by it also. Huge reservoirs, holding millions of gallons of water for cities and towns, were being clogged by algal growths. Ranchers and farmers were disturbed by the infestation of algae in stock ponds and irrigation ponds. Irrigation pumps were constantly being stopped up by the algae. At times the stock ponds became so covered by the thick mats of algae that the cattle could not reach the water to drink. I also found that many recreation facilities were being hampered by the thick algal growths. I suppose the realization that there was a need for a solution to this problem was the thing which sparked my interest enough to begin research.

I began by reading a wide variety of books and pamphlets dealing with algae. Before beginning to seek solutions to the particular problems caused by the plant, it was most important to obtain a background of general information concerning the plant. As I read, I collected facts which I thought would be useful in my study. I recorded all the facts and ideas which occurred to me on notecards as I read.

Once I had a general knowledge of the subject and the problems dealing with the subject, I organized the thoughts and facts. It was then necessary to decide a manner in which to encounter the problem. Deciding to try chemically controlling the growth of algae, I began experimentation. The problem was to find a means of destroying the plant without killing the fish and other organisms living in the water with it. The results of the tests were carefully recorded, and the tests were repeated to insure that the same results could be obtained again. I did find that the growth of algae could be controlled in a small area, but I was unable to experiment on a large scale.

This was only the beginning of the study. The more I worked with the plant, the more economically valuable I found it to be. Further study and investigation verified the idea of algae as a food source. Connected with this particular investigation was the determination of growing techniques, manners by which harvesting of algae could be done, and methods for processing the harvested plants. I also designed a model home of the future in which algae could be grown in mass, harvested, and processed auto-

Top: Included in Gregory Marchand's project (for which he received a Second Award at the 16th ISF) was a design for a system by which algae could be grown and processed for food. *Bottom:* Gregory Marchand and Robert Rychly, 1965 ISF winners, spent three weeks working on oceanographic research aboard the USNS *Sands.*

Top: Russ Mitchell, scientific director of the *Sands*, points out the midocean points that the ship will cross. *Bottom:* Gregory prepares to lower a Nansen bottle, a device that takes a water sample and a temperature reading at a specified depth.

Rychly and Marchand make ready to lower a bathythermograph to take a temperature-depth reading.

matically. Knowing that the strands of algae had tremendous surface area and were capable of producing large quantities of oxygen by photosynthesis, I began planning the design of a closed environment in which a mouse was to breathe oxygen provided by the algae. The chamber was constructed of Plexiglass and contained within it a large tank of algae in water; pellets of dry, compressed algae for the animal's food; drinking water; light sources so that the plants would have continuous light for photosynthesis; and a miniature air filter, which I designed and constructed to eliminate harmful gases from the environment. I constructed the chamber watertight so that it might be submerged beneath the water to insure that no air entered from outside the chamber. The study was successful and showed valuable possibilities for further investigation.

From going through so many books about algae, I realized that the algae in many areas had not been studied. I then decided to begin a monograph of East Texas algae. I spent weekends collecting samples, and I used spare time during weekday afternoons to photograph, draw, and identify the specimens. Sampling locations were carefully recorded on maps of the area.

Being a Scuba diver was of tremendous value in this study, as it allowed me to observe the plants in their natural habitats, and it also made collecting much easier. I have made several hundred dives since I have begun other phases of study dealing with these plants. The "Monograph of East Texas Algae" is by no means complete as yet; this particular study is still underway also. I feel that this work was not only important to the project, but it will also be useful to others in the future.

The work that I have done so far has taken three years. I worked on it as a hobby in my spare time. For the knowledge obtained, the cost was very small. I perhaps spent $50.00 for material over the three-year period.

The awards for the study were outstanding. I sincerely believe that the three most important awards which I received were self-satisfaction, experience, and increased knowledge.

7. Pseudopolyhedrons

By J. Richard Gott III

The idea for my project first occurred to me while I was thinking about the connection between polygon networks and curved surfaces, such as the surface of a sphere; zero-curved surfaces, such as a flat plane; and negatively curved surfaces, such as a saddle-shaped surface. I had known that there were polygon networks corresponding to zero- and positively curved surfaces. The polygon networks corresponding to positively curved surfaces are the regular polyhedrons (cube, tetrahedron, etc.), since their shape approximates the surface of a sphere. The regular "floor tiling" patterns, or tessellations, correspond to the planar or zero curved surfaces. One of these is the familiar checkerboard pattern made out of squares.

Since there were polygon networks corresponding to the zero and positively curved surfaces, I wondered if there could be any polygon networks corresponding to the negatively curved surfaces. Experimenting with several cardboard hexagons, I discovered that four hexagons could indeed be fitted around a point so as to form a saddle-shaped surface. I also discovered that I could add hexagons indefinitely in the same fashion to form an even larger three dimensional structure which kept folding back on itself making chambers and connecting columns. The completed network would be an infinitely large, "jungle gym"-type structure, which would fill space completely. The whole network would be made up of regular hexagons, and each and every vertex point in the network would be surrounded by four hexagons in a saddle-shaped pattern.

Encouraged by this interesting hexagon network, I tried out other polygon arrangements. In all, I found seven new polygon networks, including ones formed of triangles, of squares, and of pentagons. All were complex, repeating, three-dimensional structures. They formed a third family of regular polygon networks, on equal standing with the regular polyhedrons and the plane-filling tessellations. I decided to name these networks "pseudopolyhedrons."

At this point, I realized that I had a really good basis for a science project. I started to work trying to define the properties of the new networks and to prove useful theorems. I proved, for instance, that all the new networks were repeating and could be extended indefinitely. I also proved that the sum of the face angles around each vertex in the new networks was always greater than $360°$. (The angle at the corner of a hexagon is $120°$, and $4 \times 120° = 480° > 360°$.) This fact provided another interesting connection between the new pseudopolyhedrons and the polyhedrons and planar networks:

CLASS	CORRESPONDING CURVATURE	SUM OF ANGLES AROUND A VERTEX
polyhedron	positive	$< 360°$
planar network	zero	$= 360°$
pseudopolyhedron	negative	$> 360°$

98

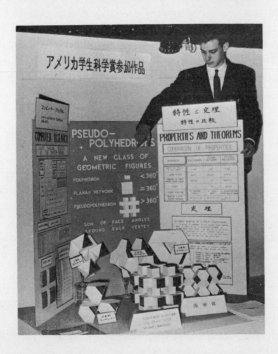

Top: For his pioneering work with pseudopolyhedrons, J. Richard Gott was selected as one of three students to represent the United States at the Japan Science Fair in Tokyo. *Bottom:* Japanese subtitles were added to his exhibit at the Tokyo fair.

In addition, I wrote a computer program which would test possible arrangements of polygons to see if it would be feasible for them to form pseudopolyhedrons. It showed that there might conceivably be as many as 21 different pseudopolyhedrons. Only seven of these 21 possibilities, however, were found to be actually constructable.

My exhibit contained posterboards showing the results of my computer work, the theorems I had proven, and the properties I had found. I also carefully made red and white cardboard models of each of the seven pseudopolyhedrons.

My project won first prize in the regional science fair at Louisville, Kentucky, and I was given a trip to St. Louis to compete in the National Science Fair-International. In St. Louis it won first prize in the Math and Computer division. Also it received awards from the U.S. Army, the U.S. Navy, and the Patent Law Association. In addition, I was selected by the U.S. Navy to represent it at the Japanese Science Fair in Tokyo. I was to be one of three students to represent the United States at this fair.

The Japanese Science Fair was held the November following the Science Fair in St. Louis. We were accompanied by two escorts from the Armed Forces and one from Science Service. We flew to Japan by way of Alaska and returned by way of Hawaii, so we really had a complete Pacific tour! The whole trip lasted two and a half weeks and was a marvelous experience. We put our projects on display at the new Tokyo Science Museum and met the other student exhibitors from Japan and several other Asian countries. While we were there, we stayed two nights with a Japanese family and visited hundreds of fascinating places. The whole trip was really wonderful.

Later, I submitted a report of my investigation to the *American Mathematical Monthly*. They pointed out that some of the work in my project had already been done by H. S. M. Coxeter in the 1930's and suggested that I resubmit my paper with this in mind. I looked up the reference and found that Dr. Coxeter had investigated three of the seven structures I had found in my project. We both had had the same basic idea concerning the new figures, but he had used somewhat more stringent criteria and thus had found fewer suitable networks. I resubmitted the article, giving appropriate reference to Dr. Coxeter's work and stating the aspects of my study that were new. The article was then accepted for publication.

Since this project was oriented around an idea rather than a set of experiments or observations, it was somewhat different from most science projects. Prior to this project, I had worked on a project concerned with applying geometrical analysis to metallic crystal structure. That project involved some computer work, and some difficult experimentation and required over two years to complete. It won a fourth place in the National Science Fair in 1964 and won second place, a $6,000 scholarship, in the Westinghouse Science Talent Search. By contrast, my pseudopolyhedron project took less than half a year to complete. In a pure mathematics project, usually the originality of the idea and the thoroughness of the resulting study are more important than the time spent or equipment used. By being observant, we can notice many interesting regularities in mathematics and find many situations where familiar methods may be used in a new way. Following up on such a regularity or situation, we can often find the basis for a fascinating and highly worthwhile science project.

U.S. Navy photo

At a reception at the Ninth Japan Science Student Award Program, left to right, are: Yosoji Kobayashi, executive vice-president of the newspaper *Yomiuri Shimbun;* ISF winner J. Richard Gott III; and Captain Robert L. Dahllof, USN, Chief of Staff to Commander, U.S. Naval Forces in Japan.

8. Effect of Radiation on the Growth and Structure of Crystals, and X-Ray Diffractions

By Randy B. Wright

An avid interest in science started at a pre-grade school age when I was recovering from polio and needed an interest or hobby to help pass the abundant idle time which was forced on me. Although a keen fascination for science continued through grade school, it was during the seventh grade that science fairs became a yearly endeavor. My first project concerned thermonuclear reactions; it was fairly successful, but its greatest value was the experience it gave to me in science fair project building and in developing methods of scientific investigation. The next three years were spent on projects concerning the transuranium elements, controlled fusion, and the synthesis of the man-made elements, respectively.

It was in the eleventh grade that the idea for the present project was formulated. Combining interests in electromagnetic radiations and in crystal growth and structure, but at the same time searching for an original and unsolved topic, I decided to do research on the effects of electromagnetic radiations on the growth and subsequent crystalline structures of crystals when exposed to various electromagnetic radiations during their growth.

The first year of work was devoted to the building of the necessary radiation sources (X rays and ultraviolet light were chosen as the radiations), to the developing of a satisfactory method for growing the crystals, and to the actual conducting of the necessary experiments essential to the gathering of research data for the project.

A homemade X-ray machine, similar to the type described in *The Amateur Scientist* by C. L. Strong, served as the X-ray source and produced X rays of 10 angstroms wavelength and furnished 5 roentgens of radiation per hour, supplied by a magnesium target tube and a 40-kilovolt power supply. Extensive precautions for radiation protection (lead shielding and radiation monitoring devices) were used to prevent possible overexposure of the harmful X rays to the operator during the machine's use. The ultraviolet light was supplied by two 250-watt Purple X light bulbs. A major problem encountered with the ultraviolet lights was the excessive amount of heat that the lights produced. The heat, if not controlled, would be detrimental to the growing crystals during the experiments. The problem was solved by employing copper-tubing cooling girdles around each light bulb and circulating cold air through the radiation chamber with a cold-air blower.

Crystals of potassium aluminum sulfate (alum) were used in the experiments. These crystals were grown by a seeded supersaturated solution method. Special crystal-growing containers, designed to absorb neither X rays nor ultraviolet light, were used in all the experiments.

During the actual experiments, growing alum crystals were exposed to one of the radiations throughout their growing period. Unexposed crystals

Randy Wright used homemade equipment to study the effects of X rays and ultraviolet light upon crystals he had grown. His projects received a First Award at the 16th ISF.

were grown simultaneously to serve as controls. The growth rates of the exposed and unexposed crystals grown in each experiment were calculated and contrasted. The macroscopic crystal structures of all the exposed crystals were carefully examined with a stereoscopic binocular microscope for possible crystalline damage or defects due to the exposure to the radiation during their growth.

The project that year was quite successful at the state science fair, but it lacked the relevant conclusions and explanations necessary for a project of the caliber of National Science Fair-International projects. The next year was spent collecting further experimental data, formulating conclusions from this data and proposing alternative explanations for the results of the experiments.

I discovered that the *ultraviolet light* reduced the exposed crystals' average growth rate by 40.1% with respect to the control crystals; the *X rays* reduced the exposed crystals' average growth rate by 73.9%. An attempt to explain the reason for these pronounced reductions in the growth rates of the exposed crystals was conducted, and two very plausible explanations with mathematical support resulted; but only further research will determine the exact single or multiple cause for these reductions.

The results of the crystal-structure studies showed no visible crystal abnormalities, but it is hoped that the utilization of X-ray diffraction and etching techniques will enable crystal defects on the atomic level, should they exist, to be studied and explained.

For a total expenditure of approximately $100, the results of this project and their potentially useful applications to crystal growing, crystal-structure theory, and solid-state physics were very inexpensive. Not only was the project a materially rewarding endeavor, as I was fortunate enough in 1965 to participate in the National Science Fair-International in St. Louis, Missouri, and while there win a First Place in the Physics Division, an Atomic Energy Commission First Award in Nuclear Related Science, and a 10-day trip to the Argonne National Laboratory, and an Air Force First Alternate Award in Physical Science, which also resulted in a summer-employment opportunity at a national research facility; but the project gave me a deep sense of personal satisfaction and achievement, and a profound, enduring interest in the expanding realm of science.

9. Developing Useful Products from Onion Skins

By Ida Jo Rheuark

Not all successful science fair projects require advanced technical knowledge, five-syllable words in explanation, nor a large outlay of money. For less than $2.50, I constructed a project that impressed judges with its originality and direct approach. Although the cost was low, a great amount of time was involved in making and testing the particle board I devised from onion skins.

It began when I was cleaning up the kitchen after dinner one night. I was wondering what I might use as a project in the approaching school science fair when I noticed that the only residue in the electric garbage disposal unit was the outer skins of onions. Here, I thought, was something exceedingly durable, which everyone discarded. Why not try to use onion skins instead of throwing them away?

My first step was to compare onion skins to paper. I found that the skins were much stronger than paper and would not dissolve in water. But skins alone were not satisfactory, so I studied the processes of making pulp paper and followed them as best I could in a home kitchen. I solicited neighbors and local grocery stores for the large amount of onion skins I needed.

The following is the method I devised to make a piece of onion skin "paper" about three by three inches: To one-half cup of chopped onion skins, add one tablespoon each of water and flour. With the hands, squeeze the mixture as flat as possible and place on waxed paper. Cover with the waxed paper. Press with a heavy instrument (I used an unheated electric iron) until it is quite thin. Place in a warm oven for about 20 minutes and then continue to let dry overnight.

Making the onion skins into a product was only the beginning. With samples of my "paper," as I first called it, I began to devise tests that would show comparisons with pulp paper and bond paper.

Later I realized that the product I had invented was more nearly comparable to cardboard and asbestos. I made numerous other experiments to include cardboard and asbestos, and I called my fabrication "onion skin particle board."

There were eight main groups of tests with subheadings for a total of 25 for each sample. I made as many as five testings in each category for each sample. In addition there were some tests I made but did not report because of unsuitability. Although I did not count the actual number of tests I made, I am sure the total was more than 500. In each test I tried to have as many controls as possible. If controls were not at all possible, I was forced to omit the report of the experiment.

The first group of tests was for the degree of *porosity* of the various samples using smoke, water, and grease. Samples on my exhibit showed the spread of two drops of colored turpentine on each of the five samples after one minute and again after five minutes.

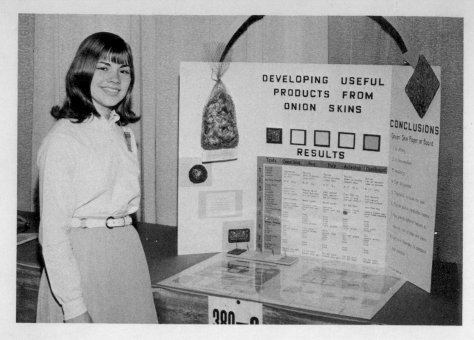

CHART

TESTS	ONION SKINS	RAG	PULP	ASBESTOS	CARDBOARD
1. Porosity					
a. Smoke	Impervious	Pervious	Pervious	Pervious	Pervious
b. Water	1 hr.-all absorbed	3½ hrs.-all absorbed	2 hrs.-all absorbed	30 min-all absorbed	1 hr.-all absorbed
c. Grease	No stain	Largest stain	Largest stain	Smallest stain	Same as asbestos
2. Bursting Strength	at 12" 100 g.	At 20" 20g.	At 12" 10 g.	At 12" 50 g.	At 20" 200 g.
3. Conductivity					
a. Heat	Almost none	Medium amount	Small amount	More than rag	Most amount
b. Cold	Almost none	Greater than pulp	Small amount	Same as pulp	Most amount
c. Current	Did not conduct	Did not conduct	Did not conduct	Did not conduct	Did not conduct
4. Reaction					
a. Flame	Same as asbestos	Burned rapidly	Burned rapidly	Did not burn	Less than rag
b. Abrasion					
1. Eraser	Surface flaked	Disturbed surface	Small hole	Surface flaked	Surface rubbed away
2. Sandpaper	Surface smoother	Surface gave way	Surface gave way	Surface torn	Surface rubbed away easily
c. Acids	Very good	Poor	Poor	Poor	Poor
5. Construction Purposes					
a. Staples	Good	Good	Good	Good	Good
b. Nails	Good	Good	Good	Good	Good
c. Glue	Good	Good	Good	Good	Good
d. Forming (box)	Fair	Good	Good	Good	Very good
e. Pliability (with heat)	Pliable	Easily pliable	Easily pliable	Fairly pliable	Pliable
6. Writing/Painting					
a. Water color	Poor	Very good	Good	Fair	Fair
b. Oil	Did not spread	Spread widely	Spread some	Did not spread	Spread widely
c. Pencil	Poor	Good	Good	Fair	Good
d. Crayon	Poor	Fair	Good	Poor	Fair
e. Ink	Poor	Good	Fair	Good	Good
7. Transmission					
a. Taste	None	None	None	None	None
b. Odor	None	None	None	None	None
8. Sealability					
a. Heat	Bonded very well	Did not bond	Did not bond	Did not bond	Did not bond
b. Binder	Bonded well	Bonded very well	Bonded very well	Did not bond	Bonded poorly

Top: Ida Jo Rheuark received a Second Award at the 16th ISF for her project, in which she developed a paper-like substance from onion skins. *Bottom:* This chart allows comparison of test results of the new substance with those of standard paper products.

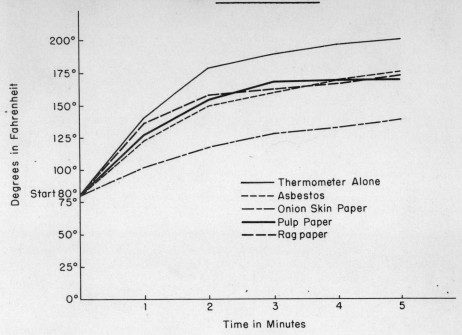

HEAT CONDUCTION

Thermometer Alone
Asbestos
Onion Skin Paper
Pulp Paper
Rag paper

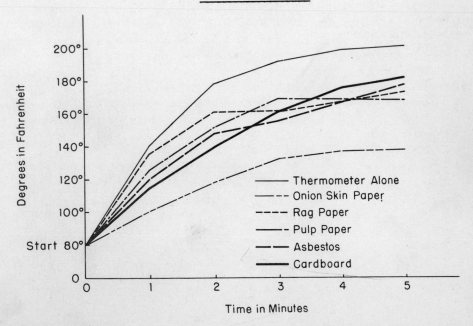

HEAT CONDUCTION

Thermometer Alone
Onion Skin Paper
Rag Paper
Pulp Paper
Asbestos
Cardboard

Samples of various papers were first placed over a 100-watt bulb, then over ice. These charts recorded temperatures after each minute for five minutes.

A second group of tests was for *bursting strength* of the materials demonstrated by dropping weights from certain measured heights onto the samples which were fastened securely on boxes.

To measure *conductivity* of heat and cold, I placed samples on a piece of glass placed respectively over a 100-watt bulb and a container of ice. The thermometer was laid on top of each sample, and a chart kept of the temperatures after each minute up to five minutes. These graphs in color formed a part of my exhibit.

Also measuring conductivity of electricity, I used a (borrowed) galvanometer, a flashlight battery, and insulated copper wire.

I showed the *reaction* of the samples to flame, abrasion, ink eraser, and sandpaper; and sulphuric, hydrochloric, and nitric acids—one drop of each on each sample.

Tests of *writing* and *painting* illustrated reactions to water colors, oil, pencil, crayon, and ink, and were shown on the exhibit with samples as well as on the large chart which dominated the center of the exhibit.

Samples of the onion skin particle board were only used on the exhibit to demonstrate the *forming* tests by being folded into squares, cones, and cups.

Tests for the *transmission* of taste and odor were described on the chart, as were the tests for *sealability* by heat and binder.

From my tests and observations I found my onion skin particle board to be strong, fire-resistant, an insulation material against heat and cold, smooth when rubbed with sandpaper, and quite attractive when waxed or varnished. I proved that it could be nailed or stapled without cracking and that it was pliable when properly prepared. I proposed making of my onion skins wall coverings, packaging materials, or other related products that require strength with lightness and good insulation and fire-resistant characteristics.

One judge wrote that mine was a "truly original Science Fair project. It is just such sparks of originality that we are trying to stimulate to occur with even greater frequency."

10. Experiments with Sonic Location

By Carolyn Ross

My project, "Experiments with Sonic Location," involved the design and construction of a device for finding the distance and direction of nearby objects by using reflected sound waves. This topic arose from an idea concerned with short-range radar devices. My original idea envisioned a device similar to the one I constructed but utilizing radio rather than sound waves. I decided to explore sonic location after learning, from a discussion with a man familiar with microwave radio, that radio waves would lead to potential problems with receiver bandwidth. Such considerations ruled out a short-range radar device built from readily available parts. The alternative was to do a similar experiment using sound waves. The medium of sound proved much easier to handle in the close quarters imposed by the space limitations of local, state, and national science fairs.

Most of my research for this project focused upon the development and operation of radar devices. When I changed to the sonic-location topic, this background, supplemented with several books on audio circuits, proved ideal. In addition to background gathered especially for this project, experience from two previous projects proved helpful. These were from the preceding two years and were concerned with binary switching circuits and television.

I began this project by dividing the topic, sonic location, into two relatively independent operations, sonic ranging and direction finding. The first operation would discover only the distance of an object. The second would provide information as to its direction. When both operations were performed simultaneously, the exact location of the object could be determined.

My first experiments were directed toward sonic ranging. The end result was to be an echo-ranging device capable of detecting objects up to ten feet away. It was to generate pulses of high-frequency sound and measure the amount of time it took for reflections to return from the object. This operation involved two circuits, one to emit pulses of sound and another to detect echoes. My main problem in this area was finding a way to produce short, square pulses. This was solved by generating sound continuously and connecting the speaker intermittently by means of an electronic switch. The sound was emitted through a high-frequency tweeter, chosen instead of an ordinary speaker because it produced a relatively narrow beam of sound At this point in the development of my experiment I observed echoes on an oscilloscope. The oscilloscope was replaced with a radar-like presentation device when I added the dimension of direction.

The other operation, the determination of direction, involved a device similar in principle to a radar scanner. It was basically a rotating turntable on which were mounted the speaker and microphone used for measuring distance. In order to visually display direction information it was necessary

Carolyn Ross designed and built this device, which determines distance and direction of an object by using reflected sound waves. Her project received a Second Award at the 17th ISF.

to have a circular sweep device which would synchronize with the turntable. Most of my problems in this area were related to devising a circular sweep circuit which could be constructed of ordinary radio and television components. The circuit which I used was somewhat novel and appears to be greatly responsible for the success of this project.

In final form, the sonic location device was mounted in a transparent plastic box with the turntable on top. Circuits were grouped according to function and mounted on separate transparent panels within the main box. After this setup was finalized, I shortened the range to about three feet. This made the project easier to demonstrate by reducing interference from background noise. In my explanation I emphasized present and potential uses of echo ranging for locating objects in water and earth.

My project cost about fifty dollars. Many of the electronic components came from old television sets. Most of the purchased equipment was special parts and display materials.

11. Polymorphous Deoxyribonucleic Acid Molecules Adapted to Experiments on the Cause, Annihilation, and Prevention of Malignancies

By Frank Raymond Rudy

For over five years I have been engaged in cancer research. At the age of twelve I began pondering the prospect of becoming a doctor; cancer, being such a controversial subject, immediately gained my interest. It was my decision to pursue cancer research throughout my high school years.

I experimented the first two years on basic research: inducing malignancies in mice with the use of chemical carcinogens, transplanting tumors, and of course doing a great deal of reading. Achieving a good foundation for research is of utmost importance. One cannot perform original research without first knowing what has already been done within the field of experimentation.

I began the main body of my research three years ago, and in the past year have obtained many conclusive findings. I originally theorized that the DNA (a chemical that is believed to control cell division) of normal body cells is mutated by some outside force, and that this mutation transforms the normal cells into malignant ones. By inducing cancer in mice and in cultured normal human tissue through injections of DNA from malignant tumors I was able to partially validate my hypothesis. The tumors that arose due to the injections of DNA were of the same cell type as the original tumors from which I extracted the DNA. This finding suggests that the foreign DNA influences the host cells' hereditary structure.

I further theorized that if tumoral DNA is chemically different from normal cell DNA, then the tumor DNA should be capable of producing an immune response in an animal. When this immune serum is removed it can be purified and tested as a possible antiserum. I encountered the problem of the similarity between tumoral and normal cell antigens. This problem was resolved by preparing an antiserum against both tumoral and normal cell DNA and then mixing the serums. The similarities were removed in the form of a precipitate.

After obtaining an anticancer DNA serum, I purified it in three separate processes; disc electrophoresis, gel immunodiffusion, and fluorocarbon extraction. When the final purified antiserum was tested on animal and human malignancies, it annihilated the tumor cells while remaining nontoxic to the normal body tissue. The antiserum can be prepared in ten days and has been found potent against all types of malignancies that were tested.

Although my research was carried on over five years, costs were held down to a minimum; first, by building as much of my own apparatus as possible and, second, by taking advantage of equipment and facilities at the city hospital. I found that most doctors and hospitals are extremely helpful and

112

For his award-winning project, Frank Rudy experimented with an anticancer serum that he had developed.

cooperative in aiding young researchers both in advisory and financial matters.

Research such as mine has a great deal of relevance to future research. Through further experiments I hope to use my findings to give proof to the virus theory of cancer origin. Presently I am experimenting with a cancer-preventitive serum. This serum is based on the DNA mutation theory. I believe that older animals (whose antibody systems have developed) are capable of rejecting injections of small quantities of tumoral DNA, which thus render them immune to at least the type of cancer for which they are inoculated.

12. *Plant Extracts and Cancer: an Attempt to Isolate Growth-Inhibiting Factors*

By Ken Emert

During my freshman and sophomore years in high school I entered local science fairs, but my projects consisted merely of models of atoms. During my sophomore year I realized that a project should be more than a model; it should be a way to probe and do research in an area of interest. Two acquaintances of mine had died recently of different forms of cancer, so I became interested in this field and began to study it.

After two months of reading and learning all that I could about cancer, I began to contact various doctors and research men. I was put in contact with Dr. Anton Lindner at the Veterans Hospital in Oklahoma City, Oklahoma, who agreed to give me a form of mouse cancer and work with me. Most of the summer was spent learning the necessary techniques, such as transplanting a tumor, preparing slides, and analyzing the effects of tumors on mice.

In my junior year, after moving to San Antonio, Texas, I received guidance from Mr. A. L. Gross of Southwest Research Institute. Every institute has its own methods or techniques so the first month was spent relearning the necessary lab procedures.

I worked for the rest of my junior year with two drugs; Methotrexate and 5-Fluorouracil. I used these known "cancer-curing" drugs to form a basis from which I could compare the curing results of my own research. On the basis of these two drugs, I defined a cured animal as one that lived for three weeks, with no tumor effects, after three-fourths of the untreated mice had died.

In my research I had read that evidence had been found that the ancient Egyptians had used garlic in the treatment of cancer. My interest aroused, I devoted the following summer and my senior year to the study of the effects of garlic and its extracts upon cancer. I began by hand pressing thirty-five pounds of garlic (a process later refined) to obtain approximately one gallon of the juice. It was necessary to have enough juice at the outset to carry through the entire experiment. Next I injected the juice into cancerous mice. All of the mice died after the first injection. I threw out the garlic and began two more times, but the results were the same. I then diluted the juice to a seventy-five percent concentration. With this solution, I had twenty percent cures. I repeated the experiment and verified the results.

My next objective was to isolate the component of the juice that was inhibiting the growth of the tumor. I dialyzed the juice to separate the large and small molecules; then freeze-dried the solutions to concentrate them. When the mice were treated with the concentrated solutions, the small-

Kenneth Emert's project, for which he received a Second Award at the 16th ISF, involved research into garlic as a cancer-curing agent.

moleculed solution killed the mice after one injection, but the large-molecculed group cured thirty-five percent of the mice. The active component which I was seeking would therefore be large-moleculed. Further study indicated that the molecule might be a protein, so the proteins were isolated from the other molecules by precipitating them out with a saturated salt solution. The protein and nonprotein groups of solution were used to treat cancerous mice and, surprisingly, the active component was *not* in the protein group. In the group from which the proteins had been eliminated the percentage of cures had risen to sixty percent.

I next eliminated the two acids DNA and RNA from the group of possible active molecules. To do so the two enzymes DNAase and RNAase were used. These two enzymes rendered the DNA and RNA respectively inactive. These solutions were then used on the mice. The group with the inactive RNA cured eighty percent of the mice. The solution with the inactive DNA did not cure any of the mice.

At this point I was able to conclude that the active "cancer-curing" component in the garlic juice was either the DNA molecule or a small molecule attached to the DNA molecule.

I spent a total of two years on this project and well over three hundred dollars. In those two years I used about five hundred mice.

I was greatly amazed at the conclusion to which I was led by my project. Even more important than the results obtained from the project, however, was what I learned from my efforts. I know now that the success of a project is determined by the ability to carry out the research in an organized manner. From a personal standpoint, the most important outgrowth of my research has been my decision to go into medical research.

13. *ATP* and *Pyromellitic Acid as Radioprotectors:*
Radioprotection and Immunosuppression

By Letantia Jankowski

Last year when I was a high school junior, I worked on a science project which dealt in one part with cellular protection from the effects of X-irradiation. I decided upon this phase of current research as a result of reading articles concerning radiobiology in science magazines and journals. The source for much of my work was *Science News*. I often wrote to scientists who were mentioned in the articles and asked for more specific information and reprints of their published papers.

The above-mentioned project gave me the necessary basic knowledge to begin my more advanced radiobiological work. I began my new project by spending the summer before my senior year doing extensive research and writing many letters. I received special permission to use a nearby college library, without which I never could have obtained all of the much-needed background information. The research on my project continued right up until the conclusion of my experiments. Including the work done last year and the time spent on research, my project took approximately one and one half years to complete.

When I was ready to start my project I began by making an outline of my proposed experiments by combining many of the ideas and theories of which I had read. Before I could begin the actual work, however, two major problems were in need of resolution. As I planned to work with large doses of radiation I had to obtain permission to use a laboratory's radioactive source free of charge. Also it was necessary for me to learn from a plastic surgeon the grafting technique that I planned to use in the second phase of my project. With the help of a friend, I obtained permission to have a technologist at a nearby industrial laboratory do the radiating for me, compliments of the company. I learned the skin-grafting procedure as a result of talking with a local plastic surgeon.

My project was divided into two experiments. The first dealt with the beneficial effects of two chemicals, ATP (adenosine triphosphate) and pyromellitic acid, on mice which had been exposed to a normally lethal dose of cobalt-60. I purchased the ATP from a New York laboratory and obtained the pyromellitic acid as a gift from a scientist in England (at that time engaged in extensive study with the chemical) to whom I wrote. After examining the mice (which were purchased from a special breeding farm) every day for thirty days, I recorded the separate and combined protective effects of both chemicals used. Pyromellitic acid, when used alone and also when the same mice were subsequently inoculated with ATP, was effective in reducing the number of deaths and minimizing the effects of the radiation.

Letantia Jankowski learned the technique of skin-grafting before beginning work on her project in the field of radiobiology, for which she won a First Award at the 16th ISF.

I used the animals which survived the first experiment in my second experiment. It is known that large doses of radiation suppress the body's immunological mechanism, thereby making it possible for animals to retain grafts that would not otherwise "take." However, such a large dose of radiation is needed that harmful side effects and even death result. Consequently, I thought that if I used the two pure strains that survived my first experiment (since they had been irradiated, yet subsequently protected) perhaps I would get complete survival of the grafts.

Complete survival was not achieved, but the radioprotected animals did exhibit an ability to prolong the graft survival significantly over the control groups. With advanced studies in the areas covered by my project, it might someday be possible to protect the world's population from the effects of radiation in the atmosphere; also it might one day be possible to perform organ transplants using a method similar to the one which I employed in my second experiment.

When my experiments were completed I recorded my work in a twenty-five-page report, which included a section of related information to enable the reader to better understand the material. My exhibit consisted of an approximately six-foot-high pegboard cut to fit a forty-eight-by-thirty-inch space. A great part of my exhibit consisted of enlarged color photographs, which, beside adding to the appearance of the exhibit, further clarified my work.

14. Establishing a Blood Group System in the Laboratory Rat

By Beth A. Romanowich

The science project that I entered in the 1966 International Science Fair in Dallas, Texas, represented four years of research and experimentation. The question which prompted the first stage of research was "Do animals have blood types like humans?" Over a period of four years this question evolved into the title of this year's project, "Establishing a Blood Group System in the Laboratory Rat." During the four years that I worked in this field, I used both mice and rats as experimental animals. This last year's work was confined to laboratory rats. New methods and techniques grew out of continual research at the local medical libraries and out of ideas gained while striving to improve the accuracy of my results. Research on this project extended throughout the four years of work. A complete bibliography of the books which I found to be most helpful to my work would include about 150 volumes, plus an even greater number of technical articles in medical and professional journals.

The amount of time expended in working on this project can only be estimated. The actual experimentation on the project which I entered in the 1966 I.S.F. began in September of 1965 and was concluded in April of 1966. During this seven-month period, an average of three hours per day was spent on experimentation and research. Though no record of expenditures was kept, an estimate of the money involved in apparatus and supplies would be approximately $175 to $200.

During the last year of experimentation and research, I encountered very few major difficulties. When I did run into a problem, I found the best way to solve it was to review each step that I had taken and look for errors and omissions. A major way in which I solved these difficulties was to decide whether the failure was due to method and technique or whether it was due to error in theory. My project advisor was most valuable in helping me review my methods and theory and in our discussions I found that none of my difficulties was insurmountable. Whenever I did encounter a problem, no matter how minor, one of the first things I did was to resort to my past research at the medical libraries, and to do more research, not just to try to find an answer to my specific question but to help prompt ideas, which often solved my problem or difficulty for me.

My project, "Establishing a Blood Group System in the Laboratory Rat," was established for the purpose of determining the existence or nonexistence of a definite and persistent pattern of blood groups in the rat, and to determine the extent of the bearing that proteins have on determining compatibility or noncompatibility of antigens and antibodies in the blood of rats. Samples of blood from laboratory rats were centrifuged to separate

121

Beth Romanowich showed blood groups to exist in the laboratory rat, and her project received a Second Award at the 17th ISF.

serum and cells. Cross-match tests were carried out and results as to whether agglutination took place were recorded. A sample of serum from each rat was subjected to protein analysis by zone electrophoresis, in order to determine the possibility of correlation between the results of the cross-match tests and the electrophoretic pattern of the serum protein. Results proved conclusively that there are *eight* distinct blood groups in the particular colony of animals used. Correlation between cross-match tests and electrophoretic patterns was evident. It is concluded that the relative amounts of the different proteins present in the serum has a great bearing on the compatibility of the antigens and antibodies present in the individual. A blood group system could be established for any colony of rats by either method; extensive cross-match tests or according to similarities of electrophoretic patterns.

Laboratory rats, proven to have a definite blood group system, could prove invaluable in research concerning organ and tissue transplant. Serological make-up has been found to have a great effect on the degree of success of transplants. Rats would also prove valuable in the field of immunochemistry and synthesis of antibodies.

15. Oral Roentgenotherapy: a Scientific Study of the Effects of X-Ray Therapy on the Oral Cavities of White Rats

By Mary L. Wade

The effects of therapeutic radiation on the oral cavities of humans is a controversial subject. I first became interested in this subject when I attended a seminar entitled "Radiation Biology" at the fifteenth International Science Fair in Baltimore, Maryland. As a result of this seminar and subsequent reading, I learned that there have been ill effects noted after therapeutic radiation of the oral cavities of humans and laboratory animals. Some of the effects which had been observed were; the quantity of saliva decreased, the saliva became a viscid mucus with a lowered acid pH, the bacteria flora of the mouth increased. Also, dental defects were described, which included a typical tooth decay which originated in the gum line areas of the teeth and spread rapidly to include the entire crown. Why these effects occurred was not known.

I wrote to numerous colleges, universities, and government and private institutes, seeking all known information on the subject. Even all this information did not reveal the answers. I undertook a study to learn the answers for myself.

The purpose of my study was to determine the effects of 3,000 R, 4,000 R, and 7,000 R of fractionated doses of X-ray irradiation on the oral cavities of white rats. Effects to be studied included alterations of the viscosity, pH, quantity, and bacteria flora of the saliva, and the histological changes in the major salivary glands, teeth, and other oral tissues.

Six caries-susceptible (strain obtained from U.S. Department of Health, Education, and Welfare) and eleven caries-resistant (ordinary laboratory animals) female white rats were used in the experiment. The rats were divided into the following six groups: A—received 3,000 R, B—Control, AC—3,000 R + 4,000 R, BD—Control, C—received 4,000 R, D—Control. Tests were run to determine a normal rat mouth before any X-ray treatments were administered. Each rat was anesthetized by an intraperitoneal injection of 28 mg/kg of Nembutal and induced to expectorate saliva by a subcutaneous injection of pilocarpine nitrate. The quantity of saliva expectorated in the first 15 minutes of salivation, the viscosity, and the pH were determined. Diluted amounts of the saliva were inoculated on Brain Heart Infusion agar plates, Blood agar plates, and Tomato Juice agar plates, which had been previously prepared. The inoculated plates were incubated, and colony counts were made, isolated and identified. X-ray films were taken of the right and left mandible and maxilla.

Fractionated doses of 3,000 R, 4,000 R, and 7,000 R of X-ray irradiation administered over the tooth and jaw area did not cause a deviation from the normal of the quantity, the viscosity, the pH, or the bacteria flora of the

Mary Wade's study of the effects of therapeutic radiation on the oral cavities of white rats received a First Award at the 17th ISF.

saliva. There were no other changes observed macroscopically or by X-ray films in Group A, which received 3,000 R. In Groups AC and C, which received 7,000 R and 4,000 R, respectively, there were no molar teeth changes which could be attributed to irradiation, but there was hair loss over the exposed area and a consistant dwarfing and sometimes disappearance of the lower left incisor. Histological sections of these incisor teeth revealed a loss of the symmetry of the dentinial tubules. Sections of the major salivary glands of the Groups A, AC, and C revealed degeneration of some of the acini.

It was concluded that 4,000 R of X-ray irradiation causes an unusual degeneration of the lower left incisor; an effect apparently independent of saliva volume, viscosity, pH, and bacteria flora. Histological studies of these incisors show severe changes in the dentin, which suggests a slow dying of the odontoblasts (the dentin-producing cells). The major salivary glands of the rats receiving 3,000 R, 4,000 R, and 7,000 R were affected by the radiation in proportion to the amount of roentgen rays received, but it was concluded that the amounts of the glands destroyed were insufficient to deter normal function.

The experiments indicated that radiation equally affects caries-susceptible and caries-resistant rats. Although the results of animal experimentation cannot be directly applied to humans, these unusual effects may prove helpful in the study of the side effects of radiation upon oral cancer.

I kept records and recorded my progress in five books—DAILY RECORDS, RAT RECORDS, BACTERIOLOGICAL RECORDS, REFERENCE MATERIALS, and PURPOSE, PROCEDURE, RESULTS, AND CONCLUSIONS. Each day I wrote in my DAILY RECORDS book the things that I had done that day—the correspondence that I had made and received, the places I had gone, the experiments I had done, and any unusual happenings in my experiment. The information contained in this book was extremely helpful to me.

The total cost of this study was about $450. I worked as a laboratory technician in a hospital laboratory and paid the expenses of my study with my earnings. I also had a $50 research grant from the Texas Academy of Science. This was a two-year study, which consumed an average of five hours a day.

16. Inhibition of Tobacco Mosaic Virus by Modified Purine and Pyrimidine Analogues

By Carolina Mederos

When I was a sophomore in high school, my biology teacher required us to sign a contract and to fulfill certain requirements for the grade we hoped to get. For an "A" you had to do a science fair project, so I started considering topics for research. At that time Dr. Fraenckel-Conrat's "creation of life in a test tube" was in furor. This immediately aroused my interest, and I began to search through magazines and to send for reprints. By science fair time, "life in a test tube" had become "The Chemical Nature of Virus," indicating the reactions of various chemicals on the infectivity of TMV. I was lucky enough to place at regional and travel to state, where I was completely overawed by all the fantastic projects. I realized how mediocre my little project was and how much research and experimentation was demanded by a real project.

That summer, as a science institute assignment, I was reading a book that mentioned 8-azaguanine as a possible plant-virus inhibitor. Later, when I was at the University of Florida for a journalism program, I spoke to a virologist about my reading and asked him to send me any reprints he could find on the subject. A few months later I received a stack of reprints and a suggestion to speak to Dr. Stephen Garnsey at USDA Research Station in Orlando about my ideas. By June after my junior year the idea of inhibiting TMV by 2-thiouracil and 8-azaguanine had materialized, and I went to speak to Dr. Garnsey. Dr. Garnsey provided texts, reprints, pots, plants, and a sharp argument to my every hypothesis.

Calbiochem gave me the purine and pyrimidine analogues I needed; I already had TMV; and I begged and borrowed all my glassware, buffers, and other chemicals from local labs. To grow my plants in controlled conditions, I borrowed a glass house from one of the public high schools and agreed to convert it to a greenhouse if I could use it for the summer and fall. When I got it, the house was covered with shrubbery and it was 120°C. inside. By the end of the summer, my friends and I had cut down the shrubbery and replaced it with gravel, whitewashed the house, knocked out windows at two ends and replaced them with exhaust fans at one end and wire cages filled with excelsior with water dripping through them at the other end. (The house was a constant 86°C.) It didn't cost me a cent—I either begged the material or got the school to pay for it (which was rather difficult at times, since I went to the rival Catholic school). After reading an article in *Life* about DMSO, I sent away for it to Crown Zellerbach and used it as a carrier agent for the analogues.

Weeks of experimentation were spent just testing indicators to see if DMSO actually did permeate throughout the plant and testing at which

As part of the preparatory work for her study, Carolina Mederos set up her own greenhouse.

concentration it was most effective. Each experiment led to a series of other experiments to determine *why* certain results were obtained. By March inhibiting TMV by purine and pyrimidine analogues was merely a tool for further experimentation. The final project, "Inhibition of Tobacco Mosaic Virus by Modified Purine and Pyrimidine Analogues" included *how* 2-thiouracil and 8-azaguanine inhibited, rather than that they merely inhibited. (There seems to be a direct reaction between analogue and virus.) It was also discovered that DMSO itself is a plant-virus inhibitor, but that in combination with an analogue it reduces, rather than increases inhibition. Today Crown Zellerbach and USDA in Orlando are experimenting with DMSO and virus inhibition.

As far as cost, I spent a year of reading reprints, a summer of putting in a greenhouse cooling system until many a midnight in a bug-ridden Florida swamp, hours of transporting plants from the greenhouse to my kitchen as hurricane flags went up, and all the experimentation and thought that goes with a science fair project. Every day from June until March I was either reading, planting, experimenting, thinking, or just watering plants; but I didn't spend a dime and I met people and had experiences that I wouldn't have gone without.

17. A System for the Photographic Recording of Cosmic Ray Tracks

By Alan C. Huber

A major part of our present knowledge concerning the fundamental nature of matter has resulted from the observation of individual nuclear particles and their interactions. Because of the significant role of this observation, there has been a great effort in the field of physics toward the development of instrumentation for the detection of these particles. The first phase of my project involved the construction of the most recent product of this effort, the spark chamber.

The possibility of working with a spark chamber was first suggested to me by an article in *Scientific American,* where I found a description of what the spark chamber actually is—a number of parallel metal plates, between which is argon, neon, or helium. When the passing of a nuclear particle is detected by auxiliary detectors, several thousand volts are applied between adjacent plates, causing a series of sparks to form. As the particle passes through the gas, it leaves a trail of ions which form a path of least resistance, and thus cause a line of sparks to delineate the particle track.

I was interested in cosmic ray work, and the advantages of the spark chamber over the more familiar cloud and bubble chambers were evident: it can show many tracks in rapid succession, with no large time delay; it is relatively simple and inexpensive; it is geometrically flexible, and the sparks are easily photographed.

At the beginning of my junior year I began the actual construction of the chamber. I roughly followed the suggestions offered by Professor James Earl of the University of Minnesota in an article in the *American Journal of Physics* (August, 1963). The design was modular, having nine units of two gaps each rather than one large unit. Each module consisted of three aluminum plates separated by two lucite frames cemented together with epoxy cement. The nine "sandwiches" thus formed were stacked vertically, separated by sheets of masonite. Gas inlets were provided through the plastic frames.

The electronics used tubes entirely, since I was less familiar with transistors and did not require their speed for cosmic ray work. The passing of the particle through the chamber is initially detected by two trays of Geiger-Muller tubes above and below the chamber. The outputs of these trays are connected to a coincidence circuit which triggers the chamber only when a particle has passed through both trays, eliminating undesirable firing of the high voltage by a particle passing through only a small part of the chamber. Approximately 9,000 volts is applied between the plates for a small fraction of a second, the time it takes to discharge the capacitors.

The construction phase of the project occupied much more time than I

Construction of a spark chamber, a device only recently developed by physicists, was the major effort in Alan Huber's project. He received a Second Award at the 16th ISF.

had anticipated spending on it. Only partial success in operation was achieved by the time of the regional science fair. Of course, all attempts to demonstrate even this limited success for the judges were in vain. Although I fully intended to continue work on the project in any case, winning the Navy Science Cruiser Award was an added impetus.

As I continued work on the project, perfection of the apparatus continued to occupy much time. Advice on the problems I encountered was given by my physics teacher as well as a professor with whom I was acquainted. I discovered, however, that the most effective means to the solution of a problem was to read what others had done and then to experiment with the various possibilities.

Eventually, I attained a reasonable degree of efficiency in the operation of the chamber. About 80 percent of the gaps fired when a particle passed. Attempts at improving this figure continued to take a considerable portion of my time, however.

With the approach of the science fair I desired to at least begin the research on cosmic rays for which I had constructed the chamber. I therefore set up a photographic system for recording the tracks. For this purpose I used a second-hand Kodak movie camera, bought for $5. Eight-mm film actually has a 16-mm sensitive width (it is reversed halfway through in normal operation). I modified the camera to take photographs on the entire 16-mm width and set up a system of mirrors to reflect both a front and side view of the chamber to the camera, which was mounted above. It was operated in total darkness with no shutter, the sparks being self-illuminating. Each time the chamber fired, a circuit automatically advanced the film one frame, so I was able to leave the room while the tracks were being recorded. The resulting photographs were developed immediately and projected with a modified 16-mm projector (which was also purchased for $5).

The question I was attempting to answer in this research project concerns the so-called geomagnetic effects. Although the origin of cosmic rays is not known, it is known that these high-speed protons and heavy nuclei enter the earth's magnetic field isotropically, or in equal numbers from every direction. After passing through the earth's field, however, they are no longer isotropic. Because of their positive charge, more enter at the poles than at the equator and more from the west than from the east. I attempted to determine whether this directionality could be detected in the secondary cosmic rays which reach the earth, products of repeated interactions of the primaries and successively produced secondaries with molecules in the atmosphere. The procedure followed was to check each track and record the direction it deviated from the vertical in the east-west and north-south planes.

A shortage of time severely limited my work. Of about 10,000 photographs taken, only 3,000 were analyzed, and the results are far from conclusive. The figures obtained showed what appeared to be geomagnetic effects of magnitude several times that theoretically predicted and observed by others.

This is not easily explained, and although the past year has been too busy, I hope to continue my research during the coming school year to obtain more conclusive data.

A great deal of time and about $200 were devoted to this project. The satisfaction derived was quite sufficient in itself to make the work worthwhile. Financially, the project did yield a profit after competition in several science fairs and contests. This was far from being the most important result of my effort, however.

The results of the National Science Fair have enabled me to assist in more advanced work in the field of cosmic ray research. As part of the Air Force First Award, I was given a job at the Air Force Cambridge Research Laboratories in Bedford, Massachusetts, for the summer, where I worked with nuclear emulsions, photographic material for recording nuclear tracks, which had been flown in balloons, rockets, and satellites. I am presently working with the same group at the physics research division of Emmanuel College, in Lexington, Massachusetts.

18. The Development of a Science Fair Project

By Edward Charles Svendsen

In May, 1966, I entered a paper, "A Derivation of the Maxwell-Lorentz Equations," in the International Science Fair in Dallas, Texas. Despite the apparent success of my project, which won a second place in physics in the regular ISF competition and special awards from the Atomic Energy Commission and the National Aeronautics and Space Administrations, the development of my science fair project was a very frustrating process, for reasons which I will explain shortly.

The goal of modern theoretical physics is to describe the complexities of nature in terms of the relatively simple interactions of the so-called "elementary particles." These simpler interactions must be described with the framework of quantum mechanics, a branch of physics which has been remarkably successful in "explaining" nature. Physicists have found only four fundamental forces: gravitational, weak, electromagnetic, and strong interactions. My project is concerned with electromagnetic interactions.

Electromagnetic interactions have been successfully treated in the theory known as quantum electrodynamics, a theory extensively developed by Feynman, Schwinger, and Tomonaga, who shared the 1965 Nobel Prize in Physics for their contributions. Quantum electrodynamics represents a merging of relativity, quantum mechanics, and electromagnetic theory. When the synthesis is attempted, many difficulties are produced. The three Nobel laureates managed to avoid, but not eliminate, these difficulties to the extent that the present theory of quantum electrodynamics is characterized by remarkable agreement with experiment. Whereas nuclear forces are only poorly understood, we can confidently say that electromagnetic forces are well understood.

When I became interested in electromagnetic theory in January, 1965, I knew little about the subject and nothing about quantum electrodynamics. I knew a little about calculus but nothing about solving partial differential equations. Similarly, I knew a little about vectors but nothing about tensors. In short, I lacked the mathematical background for the task before me. Since each step in my physical understanding had to be accompanied by increased mathematical knowledge, I found myself spending as much time on learning new math as on learning new physics. Since theoretical physics is entirely mathematical, this is to be expected.

At first I wanted to know why two electrons repel each other. I proceeded to formulate a rather naive model of electrostatic force based upon the emission and absorption of particles. I then tried to explain magnetic forces by bringing in results from relativity known as force transformations. I then tried to explain a phenomenon known as quantum mechanical tunnelling. No matter what mental gymnastics I performed, I couldn't make my naive

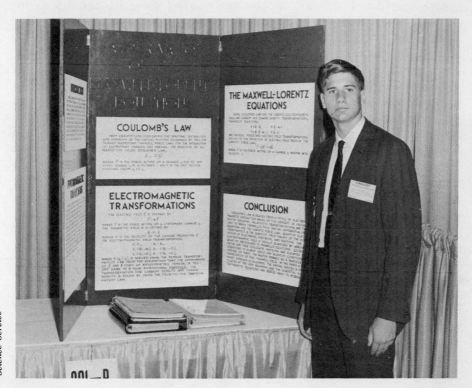

For his theoretical project, "A Derivation of the Maxwell-Lorentz Equations," Edward Svendsen received a Second Award at the 17th ISF.

model explain experimental facts. Therefore I rejected the model. In doing so I also rejected classical determinism.

Meanwhile I had become more acquainted with quantum mechanics and electromagnetic theory. I had learned that the most important equations of classical electromagnetic theory are Maxwell's equations and the Lorentz force law. I had also learned of an entity known as the virtual photon, a "particle" which I will not attempt to describe, since its meaning is intimately connected with relativistic quantum field theory, at best a very difficult subject. I then decided to derive Maxwell's equations and the Lorentz force law from a model of electromagnetic interaction based upon the concept of the virtual photon. This last phase of project development was as frustrating as the first phase, but I finally succeeded.

During the development of my paper I had no contact with theoretical physicists, except for two brief talks relatively late in the development. Consequently I never knew exactly where I was going. I wasted much time and effort. Certainly anyone interested in doing a project in theoretical physics should see a theoretical physicist as soon as possible for advice. There are many benefits to be gained from studying theoretical physics. However, it is not for the mathematically timid, for one cannot even really begin to study the subject without knowing some calculus. But the necessary mathematical knowledge can be gained.

Theoretical physics is an exciting field. In this century it has attracted such fine minds as Einstein, Bohr, Shroedinger, Heisenberg, Dirac, and Fermi. Today theoretical physics is central to man's attempt to understand nature.

19. An Investigation of Trichinosis in Non-Mammalian Vertebrates

By Dena Ditzenberger

I first became interested in parasitology in my freshman biology class. This interest was rekindled in my sophomore year zoology class, especially in the area of parasitic roundworms, due to their rather complicated life cycles. The trichina worm (Trichinella spiralis) was stressed as a danger to man and all other meat-eating mammals. While doing some later research into the life cycle of these roundworms, I found that the disease trichinosis is greatly feared in the polar regions where the natives contract the disease from the whales, seals, bears, and other mammals that inhabit the area. I began wondering how the whales, who are on a marine diet, could possibly come in contact with this disease if meat-eating *non*-mammalians couldn't carry it too. This, and the fact that some birds are also carnivorous, was the entire basis for my research.

A rather crude outline was made, thinking it better to try one experiment, check the results, and then continue from there.

A search through the local university and public libraries revealed no previous research done with cold-blooded animals and only a small amount with meat-eating birds. A complete bibliography and appendix may be found at the end of this report.

Summary

The most significant results obtained in each experiment may be stated briefly as follows:

Test One: In chicks who were introduced to the Trichinella cysts at age 19 days by feeding rat-infected meat, the presence of living larvae in large numbers in the intestinal tract over an extended period of time seemed to seriously affect the general health of the birds. The symptoms were: a slightly lower weight gain than the control, loss of feathers, bad disposition, drooping wings, and the development of eye tumors. Adult worms were not observed in intestinal examinations nor were cysts in the muscles.

Test Two: The results were more profound with the chicks on this test in which the infected meat feedings were begun at the age of two days and in which a soft diet was maintained throughout the test period. Microscopic examination of the intestinal contents revealed not only living larvae but also living adult trichina worms containing eggs. The infestation was severe enough to cause death in 33% of the test group. Direct tissue examinations revealed no visible muscular cysts. Some larvae were detected in tissue residues treated with tryspin.

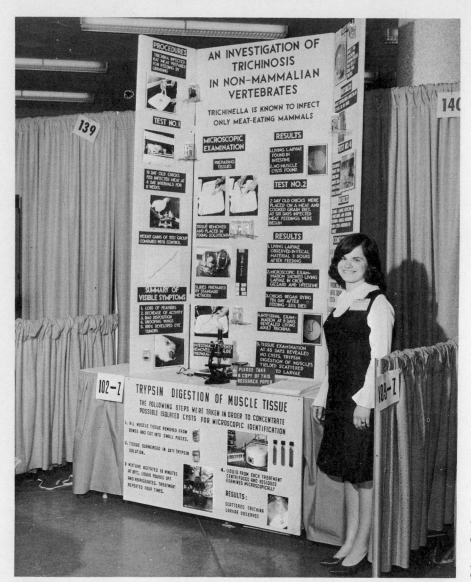

Dena Ditzenberger's study of trichinosis in cold-blooded animals and meat-eating birds involved research into areas not previously covered in the literature. She received a First Award at the 17th ISF.

Test Three: This experiment is one of the most interesting because no evidence of previous research involving fish could be found, even though fish are meat eaters. The fish in this experiment were capable of freeing the trichina larvae from their cysts and harboring them in their intestines to adulthood. Since many mammals eat fish raw, sometimes even man, the presence of the living larvae in the fishes' intestine is enough to establish the fish as a potential carrier of trichinosis.

I received assistance only as far as being taught to do things for myself.

In the preparation of slides to observe muscle-tissue samples, a professor at Indiana State University instructed me on procedures, and then I was on my own. My sponsor, Mr. Harry Wunker, Science Department Head, Garfield High School, and I discussed plans for the project and he advised me in the correct technique of research. He assisted me in dissection until I was capable of doing it alone.

There were no great difficulties concerning my project. Cost was the only big obstacle until I received a one-hundred dollar research grant from the Indiana Heart Association. This was spent mostly for the rats we used to infect our animals. This cost obstacle could be overcome by infecting a good supply of rats in advance of the actual experimentation. I didn't realize so many rats would be used and after I did know there wasn't enough time for this method.

I worked on this project about seven and a half months, on the average of two hours each school day. Towards the end of my experiment I spent three or four hours in the lab, but a lot of that time went into the making of a display.

Conclusions

1. Although no direct relationship can be shown between the various symptoms noted in test one and trichinosis, it would appear that the presence of living trichina in the intestines of chickens affects the general health of the animals.

2. Young chicks may die from the presence of large numbers of trichina larvae and adults in their intestines.

3. Mice can contract trichinosis from eating excreta of chickens that have living trichina larvae in their intestines.

4. Fish in warm, garbage-polluted waters, if they have been introduced to trichina cysts, could carry the infection to mammals if eaten.

5. Muscular cysts, formed in non-mammalian vertebrates, have been too few to be observed by random tissue examination.

6. Chicken tissue residues after treatment with tryspin yielded a small number of larvae, thus establishing the completion of the Trichinella spiralis life cycle in young chickens.

For this project I received the First Place, Zoological Division for Girls at the International Science Fair, 1966, Dallas, Texas.

20. A Closed Ecological System

By Carin C. Clamann

Science fiction, with its intriguing allusions to life on distant planets, travels through space and time, and the more realistic idea of future space flights with a duration of months or years, had always fascinated me. Would it be possible for me to keep even fairly simple animals alive in a completely closed ecological system, inclusive of feeding, removing and utilizing wastes, and providing sufficient oxygen? A complicated system using warm-blooded animals such as rats, mice, or guinea pigs would give rise to the following complications: (1) Algae must be processed; they cannot be consumed directly. (2) Feces and urine cannot be fed directly into an algal colony; they also must be processed. (3) In the gas exchange with algae, the air will always be 100 percent water-vapor-saturated. A drying mechanism must be provided in order to promote healthy animals. Such a drying mechanism can be complicated if no water is to be lost. The above disadvantages may be eliminated by the choice of a fish as the vertebrate. Gas exchange occurs in the water common to the fish and plant, likewise the exchange of other wastes. This left me with the problem of choosing a suitable fish and algae. After several attempts, I discovered that the common goldfish and a common pond algae (Calothrix and Spyrogyra) were a perfect combination.

Researching and mapping out the project was a varied hunt that started in science fiction books, and led through textbooks, school, home and public libraries, magazines, personal contact with authorities on the field, and ended in the correlation of information and the drawing out of important information and the discarding of that which did not directly apply to the project, but which was necessary in forming the ideas leading up to it. The primary research took about six months, but I never stopped researching and trying for improvements. Reading up on environmental systems helped put in some last-minute improvements as well as giving more concise and meaningful answers to the ever rising questions from parents, friends, teachers and later, judges.

My project was surprisingly inexpensive. The included, labeled diagram shows the assembled project; the expenses for the items are detailed on p. 144. Common household articles, such as glass olive containers and an ordinary goldfish bowl made up most of the equipment; some were borrowed or constructed by a friend who volunteered his glass-blowing abilities; the rest was bought in a local hardware store. My project took much of my spare time, designing and building were fit into odd moments, experimenting into a regular time schedule. Progress was recorded in a log, so that no details would be forgotten. This log later proved very useful; it served as a reminder of what I had done, how it was done, and the exact day it was done on. This log later became the basis of my project report.

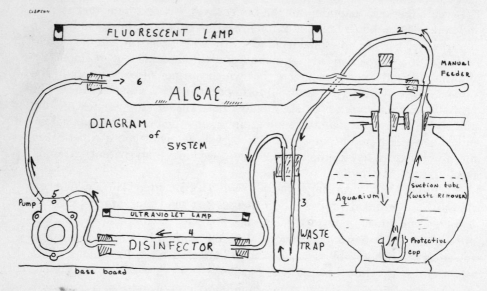

Top: Carin Clamann designed and built a closed ecological system in which gold-fish feed on algae and gases are exchanged in the water common to both. This project won a First Award at the 16th ISF. *Bottom:* In this diagram the functioning of the system can be clearly traced.

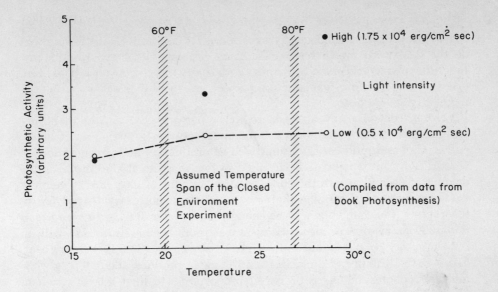

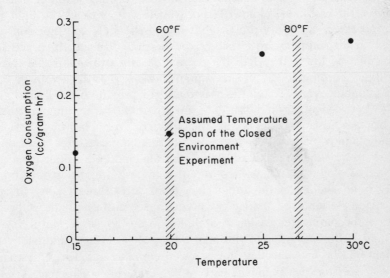

Top: Photosynthetic activity of green algae as a function of environmental temperature and light intensity. (Note: Between 10° C. and 27° C., only at high light intensity, the algal gas-exchange rate increases by about one half.) *Bottom:* Oxygen consumption of a goldfish, expressed as cubic centimeters per gram of body weight per hour, as a function of environmental temperature. (Note: Between 20° C. and 27° C., oxygen consumption increases almost twofold.)

The work itself needed mostly experience for assistance. But authorities on the field were invaluable in discussing problems as they arose. Many times the advice I received from these authorities was to consult a book, but just as often a helpful ear and experienced eye could detect an answer I might have overlooked.

For best control, plants and fish are kept separately. By varying quantities of algae and the flow rate of water, balance between growth rate of algae and food consumption of the fish as well as production and consumption of O_2 and CO_2 can be regulated. The algal system must be able to produce the amount of O_2 and absorb the corresponding amount of CO_2. Pre-calculated data was used to determine the amount of algae necessary to provide a favorable gas exchange as well as enough food. According to this information 1000 grams of wet algae produces (at room temperature, and with a light intensity of 1200 foot-candles) about 800 cc O_2. The two fluorescent lamps at the distance of 8 inches from the algae produce about $\frac{1}{100}$ of this intensity (photosynthesis is produced proportional to light intensity, when all other factors are equal), or 8 cc O_2 per hour. Since 2.6 cc O_2 are needed, 500 g wet algae would suffice. The food consumption is expressed in calories and will result in the food consumption in weight units if the calorie value of the food in question is known. Approximately four times the light intensity is necessary to satisfy the twofold increases of O_2 consumption of the goldfish at the temperature as shown on the first diagram. In practice, the lamps must be lowered to half the present distance to quadruple the light intensity, according to the inverse square law. A H_2O flow rate of 500 cc for 10 minutes every 30 minutes was found to provide a satisfying gas exchange between algae and fish. The intermediate rather than continuous flow has the advantage to permit the algae to "rest" between periods of exchange and provide for feeding and emergency procedures. It also offers the disinfector time to irradiate the debris collected and render it harmless.

Closed ecological systems are rapidly gaining importance. From the underground shelter to the submarine, from suboceanic colony to spaceship, space station, and planetary colony, a self-sustaining life-supporting system is becoming increasingly vital. For basic research, simple systems will yield better insight into the relationship of existing parameters. Such a system will be an important link to more complex systems. A system like the one presented can be developed into an even more effective system by the addition of mollusks or other invertebrates for human consumption.

EXPENSES FOR ECOLOGICAL SYSTEM:

1. Aquarium .... $ 1.80
2. Fluorescent lamps 4.00
3. Ultraviolet lamps 5.00
4. Miscellaneous (screws, poster paper, pegboard, rubber tubing, paint, glass tubing, wire, rubber corks, varnish, and
   aluminum ribbing for poster) 12.00
   Total $20.00

AWARDS (SENIOR HIGH SCHOOL):

1. Alamo District Science Fair (1964)
   First Army Award
   National Aeronautics and Space Administration Award
2. 15th International Science Fair (1964)
   Alternate Army Award
3. Alamo District Science Fair (1965)
   First Grand Prize
   NASA Award
   Bexar County Medical Association Award
   Air Force Aerospace Medicine Award
   American Institute of Aeronautics and Astronautics Award
4. Texas Catholic Science Fair (1965)
   Second Place
5. Converse Grange Science Award (1965)
6. 16th International Science Fair (1965)
   First Place

21. A Theory of Artin Braids

By Michael Levintow

My science project was suggested by the elementary school discussion of a mathematical system (a set of elements and a procedure for operating any element by another) that was called "Artin braids." The elements of the system are six geometrical forms, called braids. Each braid consists of two rows of three points connected in pairs by line segments. To operate

The Six Artin Braids

Procedure for Operating

a braid X by braid Y, join the lower row of X to the upper row of Y by corresponding coordinates (1 to 1, 2 to 2, 3 to 3). Then replace each pair of segments now connecting the upper row of X to the lower row of Y by a single connecting segment. The result must always be a large-sized representation of one of the braids, defined to be X operated by Y (XoY). After the system was defined, the group properties (closure, associativity, existence of an identity, existence of the inverse) were demonstrated to hold.

My first step in research was to generalize the system. Clearly the six forms comprise the possible one-to-one correspondences between two sets of three points, established by segments. Why not construct a generalized system whose elements comprise the possible one-to-one correspondences between two sets of n points, having an operation analogous to the joining procedure?

Then, in the generalized system, would the group properties hold? Are there any other properties of the generalized elements or operation? After some investigation, the group properties and some others seemed intuitively valid in the system but lacked rigorous proof. It occurred to me that some means of algebraic representation of the elements and operation might provide the verifying tool. I discovered that an Artin braid of any order n (the number of points in each row) is representable as a permutation of

n objects. For example, the order 4 braid can be represented

by the permutation $\begin{pmatrix} 1 & 2 & 3 & 4 \\ 4 & 2 & 1 & 3 \end{pmatrix}$, where the upper row of the array rep-

Michael Levintow's theoretical project received a Second Award at the 17th ISF.

resents coordinates of upper-row braid points, and the lower row, coordinates of corresponding lower-row points. Generally speaking, an order n

Artin braid can be represented as $\begin{pmatrix} 1 & 2 & 3 & \ldots & n \\ a_1 & a_2 & a_3 & \ldots & a_n \end{pmatrix}$ with suitable restrictions on the variables.

Then a very important step was taken. I realized that a slight modification of this notation, in which a subscripted variable a_x was replaced by the *function* $f(x)$, also provided a convenient means of representing the operation. The representations of elements and operation were incorporated into two axioms:

A1. An Artin braid of order n is equivalent to a function of the form

$$\begin{bmatrix} 1 & 2 & 3 & \ldots & n \\ f(1) & f(2) & f(3) & \ldots & f(n) \end{bmatrix}$$—the ordered pairs of the function are ar-

ranged in tabular form; the domain elements are listed in the upper row, the corresponding range elements in the lower row—possessing the properties A) $x = y = {>} f(x) = f(y)$,* and B) $[f(1), f(2), f(3) \ldots f(n)] = (1, 2, 3 \ldots n)$.

A2. $\begin{bmatrix} 1 & 2 & 3 & \ldots & n \\ f(1) & f(2) & f(3) & \ldots & f(n) \end{bmatrix} \circ \begin{bmatrix} 1 & 2 & 3 & \ldots & n \\ g(1) & g(2) & g(3) & \ldots & g(n) \end{bmatrix} =$

$$\left\{ \begin{array}{ccccc} 1 & 2 & 3 & \ldots & n \\ g[f(1)] & g[f(2)] & g[f(3)] & \ldots & g[f(n)] \end{array} \right\}.$$

From these axioms theorems could be deduced.

Using the axioms, all the group properties were proved as follows:

For any braids $\begin{bmatrix} 1 & 2 & \ldots & n \\ f(1) & f(2) & \ldots & f(n) \end{bmatrix}$, $\begin{bmatrix} 1 & 2 & \ldots & n \\ g(1) & g(2) & \ldots & g(n) \end{bmatrix}$,

and $\begin{bmatrix} 1 & 2 & \ldots & n \\ h(1) & h(2) & \ldots & h(n) \end{bmatrix}$,

$$\left\{ \begin{bmatrix} 1 & 2 & \ldots & n \\ f(1) & f(2) & \ldots & f(n) \end{bmatrix} \circ \begin{bmatrix} 1 & 2 & \ldots & n \\ g(1) & g(2) & \ldots & g(n) \end{bmatrix} \right\} \circ$$

$$\begin{bmatrix} 1 & 2 & \ldots & n \\ h(1) & h(2) & \ldots & h(n) \end{bmatrix} = \left\{ \begin{array}{cccc} 1 & 2 & \ldots & n \\ g[f(1)] & g[f(2)] & \ldots & g[f(n)] \end{array} \right\} \circ$$

$$\begin{bmatrix} 1 & 2 & \ldots & n \\ h(1) & h(2) & \ldots & h(n) \end{bmatrix} = \begin{pmatrix} 1 & & n \\ h\{g[f(1)]\} & \ldots & h\{g[f(n)]\} \end{pmatrix}.$$

---

* This restriction is not absolutely necessary if "function" is understood to imply that, for each domain element, there corresponds *exactly one* range element.

$$\begin{bmatrix} 1 & 2 & \dots & n \\ f(1) & f(2) & \dots & f(n) \end{bmatrix} \circ \left\{ \begin{bmatrix} 1 & 2 & \dots & n \\ g(1) & g(2) & \dots & g(n) \end{bmatrix} \circ \right.$$

$$\left. \begin{bmatrix} 1 & 2 & \dots & n \\ h(1) & h(2) & \dots & h(n) \end{bmatrix} \right\} = \begin{bmatrix} 1 & 2 & \dots & n \\ f(1) & f(2) & \dots & f(n) \end{bmatrix} \circ$$

$$\left\{ \begin{matrix} 1 & 2 & \dots & n \\ h[g(1)] & h[g(2)] & \dots & h[g(n)] \end{matrix} \right\} =$$

$$\left(\begin{matrix} 1 & \dots & n \\ h\{g[f(1)]\} & \dots & h\{g[f(n)]\} \end{matrix} \right) . \text{Q.E.D.}$$

Another class of theorems involves geometrical transforms of braids. The rectangular arrangement of points in a braid suggested transforms of rotation around the horizontal axis, vertical axis, and center of the rectangle. The most important theorem I discovered was: For any order, the set of braids invariant under the vertical transform forms a subgroup under the operation. All were provable using the axioms.

When I was constructing a table of operation (a table listing all possible products of two braids of a given order), certain patterns in the table became apparent. I wondered if there existed any method of generating the table (possibly based on these patterns) which avoided performing the operation of each product. Such a method would be particularly valuable, since the number of entries $[(n!)^2]$ for order (n) increases enormously with the order. A recursive procedure was devised in which the table for order n braids was generated from that of order n-1. In other words, all tables of operation could theoretically be generated from the trivial order 1 table of one entry! Most important, *the validity of the procedure could be established using the Artin braid axioms* (along with properties of integers independent of braid theory).

So the Artin braid axioms not only provided the tool for proving theorems but established a useful method of table generation. Their value became even more apparent after reading the original research of Artin.[*] He lacked an axiomatic method for proving theorems, such as the group properties (although, since he primarily investigated three-dimensional braids—considerably more complex than mine—such an omission is not surprising). To prove each of his theorems, a special technique had to be devised.

Although all research was original, valuable assistance in constructing my exhibit was given by the Kramer family of Bethesda, Maryland. Mr. Kramer built a mechanical device for operating Artin braids, which was a considerable improvement over the traditional construction. The traditional

---

[*] Emil Artin (1898–1962) was a German mathematician who came to the United States during the 1930's. For a while he taught at the universities of Princeton and Indiana, lecturing on group theory and related topics. He started investigating braid theory as part of a more general investigation of the theory of knots.

device required removing a row of thumbtacks to perform the operation. If the operation was repeated, the thumbtacks often flew out of place prematurely. His device replaced thumbtacks by pegs mounted on a movable bar, thus sidestepping the difficulty. In addition, he helped me locate Artin's original papers.

I worked several years on the project. However, most of the work (including discovery of functional notation and first use of axioms) was done in the summer and fall of 1965. Earlier research primarily involved generalization of the system and investigation of theorems.

It should be mentioned that the Artin braid system is a valuable teaching aid in introducing group theory. The system is representative of finite groups, and its group properties can be easily and convincingly demonstrated.

AWARDS (SENIOR HIGH SCHOOL):

1. 25th Westinghouse Science Talent Search
   Top 40
2. Montgomery County, Md., Science Fair (1966)
   Grand Prize
3. 17th International Science Fair (1966)
   Second Place

22. Organic Phosphates versus Chlorinated Hydrocarbons, with Special Emphasis on Toxicity; Internal and Histopathological Effects on Certain Aquatic Animals

By Susan L. Campbell

Water pollution, a serious problem, also offers many areas of fascinating research. In 1964, one phase of this research was brought to my attention by a professor at Louisiana State University. He suggested that I work with the effects of insecticides on aquatic animals. For one year I studied the effects of aldrin on the *Lebistes reticulatus* or common guppy. For this project I was awarded a trip to the 16th National Science Fair in St. Louis, Mo. By talking to professionals who work with this chemical, I found many new problems in the same area. During the next few weeks I read research papers, many books, and I corresponded with several researchers who were working in this same area.

From my research I found that there are two main groups of insecticides, organic phosphates and chlorinated hydrocarbons. Much research has been conducted using one group or the other, but no one had actually compared the two groups. This was my purpose, to make a satisfactory comparison of organic phosphates and chlorinated hydrocarbons showing relative toxicity; internal and histopathological effects.

By studying research conducted with each group individually, I was able to decide on a hypothesis. Knowing that organic phosphates attack the nervous system by destruction of the enzyme cholinesterase, it could be stated that the test animals would undergo several periods of highly erratic movements, including loss of equilibrium and rapid swimming. However, from previous research that I had conducted with a chlorinated hydrocarbon I had observed similar symptoms of less density than that described by other authors using organic phosphates. Having observed this it was necessary to state that both groups would show erratic movements but that they would be less intense in the chlorinated hydrocarbon groups. On the other hand, chlorinated hydrocarbons are stored in the body fat of the animals, and it could be stated that the fat tissue would be damaged and the insecticide would be stored in the body fat. Again, however, it is known that any impurity can be stored in the organs rich in fat. So it was necessary to state that the fat tissue in the organic phosphate group would show less damage to the fat tissue than the chlorinated hydrocarbons. From other research papers, I compared their results with organic phosphates against my results with chlorinated hydrocarbons and determined that the chlorinated hydrocarbons would be the most toxic. The hypothesis can thus be stated:

1. The organic phosphate group will show more erratic movements of greater frequency and severity.

A study of the effects of various insecticides on aquatic animals brought Susan Campbell a Second Award at the 17th ISF.

2. The chlorinated hydrocarbon group will show more damage to the organs rich in fat.

3. The chlorinated hydrocarbons will be the most toxic.

These are only educated guesses, which I set out to prove or disprove.

Three representatives of each insecticide group were used. These were chosen on the basis of usage in the area and established toxicity. For the organic phosphates; diazinon, vapona, and malathion were used. For the chlorinated hydrocarbons; aldrin, dieldrin and chlordane. Two test animals were selected, the *Carassius auratus* or goldfish because of its accessibility, and the *Lepomis macrochirus* or bluegill because of its use as a game fish.

The animals were tested at three dilutions and a control. The dilutions

ORGANIC PHOSPHATES

Insecticide	Test animal	Dilution	Time	Deaths
Diazinon	C.A.	8ppm	86 hours	2
Diazinon	C.A.	4ppm	120 hours	0
Diazinon	C.A.	1pp^{100}/m	120 hours	0
Diazinon	C.A.	Control	120 hours	0
Diazinon	L.M.	8ppm	23 hours	2
Diazinon	L.M.	4ppm	35 hours	2
Diazinon	L.M.	1pp^{100}/m	120 hours	0
Diazinon	L.M.	Control	120 hours	0
Vapona	C.A.	8ppm	120 hours	0
Vapona	C.A.	4ppm	120 hours	0
Vapona	C.A.	1pp^{100}/m	120 hours	0
Vapona	C.A.	Control	120 hours	0
Vapona	L.M.	8ppm	120 hours	0
Vapona	L.M.	4ppm	120 hours	0
Vapona	L.M.	1pp^{100}/m	120 hours	0
Vapona	L.M.	Control	120 hours	0
Malathion	C.A.	8ppm	120 hours	0
Malathion	C.A.	4ppm	120 hours	0
Malathion	C.A.	1pp^{100}/m	120 hours	0
Malathion	C.A.	Control	120 hours	0
Malathion	L.M.	8ppm	5 hours	2
Malathion	L.M.	4ppm	6 hours	2
Malathion	L.M.	1pp^{100}/m	120 hours	0
Malathion	L.M.	Control	120 hours	0

used were 8ppm*, 4ppm, and 1pp^{100}/m**. A test limit of one hundred twenty hours was set to prevent loss of insecticide due to evaporation. All tests were conducted at 20 degrees Centigrade in water similar to that used in the stock aquarium. All test animals were conditioned in the stock aquarium for two weeks as to water, temperature, diet, and feeding time. Two fish were used in each test. Hourly checks were made and recorded.

After a test was terminated by death or test limit, one sample of body fat was removed for preservation and another for microscopic examination. Several blood smears were made to determine any visible damage to the blood cells. At the conclusion of the tests, the results were compared by use of the charts shown on pages 153 and 154.

Chlorinated Hydrocarbons

Insecticide	Test animal	Dilution	Time	Deaths
DDT	C.A.	8ppm	20 hours	2
DDT	C.A.	4ppm	24 hours	2
DDT	C.A.	1pp^{100}/m	120 hours	0
DDT	C.A.	Control	120 hours	0
DDT	L.M.	8ppm	16 hours	2
DDT	L.M.	4ppm	23 hours	2
DDT	L.M.	1pp^{100}/m	120 hours	0
DDT	L.M.	Control	120 hours	0
Aldrin	C.A.	8ppm	120 hours	0
Aldrin	C.A.	4ppm	120 hours	0
Aldrin	C.A.	1pp^{100}/m	120 hours	0
Aldrin	C.A.	Control	120 hours	0
Aldrin	L.M.	8ppm	120 hours	0
Aldrin	L.M.	4ppm	120 hours	0
Aldrin	L.M.	1pp^{100}/m	120 hours	0
Aldrin	L.M.	Control	120 hours	0
Chlordane	C.A.	8ppm	14½ hours	2
Chlordane	C.A.	4ppm	15½ hours	2
Chlordane	C.A.	1pp^{100}/m	120 hours	0
Chlordane	C.A.	Control	120 hours	0
Chlordane	L.M.	8ppm	12½ hours	2
Chlordane	L.M.	4ppm	14½ hours	2
Chlordane	L.M.	1pp^{100}/m	120 hours	0
Chlordane	L.M.	Control	120 hours	0

* ppm—parts per million.
** pp^{100}/m—parts per 100 million.

Conclusions could then be made. Chlordane and DDT were the most toxic insecticides. The *Lepomis macrochirus* was the most sensitive of the test animals. By observation it was concluded that the organic phosphate group showed more intense erratic movements. By dissection it was shown that the chlorinated hydrocarbons were stored in the body fat, and by microscopic examination it was shown that they did more damage to the fat tissue than the organic phosphates. The chlorinated hydrocarbons were the most toxic. The conclusion can thus be stated:

1. The organic phosphate group showed more intense erratic movements.
2. The chlorinated hydrocarbons showed more damage to the organs rich in fat.
3. The chlorinated hydrocarbons were the most toxic.

The hypothesis was not proven incorrect and is, therefore, tentatively accepted as the correct explanation.

I am now working on a continuation of this project. It will concern a comparative study of the two groups mentioned. I am studying the magnification of these substances in a food chain. This research will be conducted for one year and I shall enter it at our regional fair in March.

No matter how busy you are, you must try to do a science project. The rewards are many. Not only do you receive a monetary award but you gain self-confidence and pride of achievement. At the International level you will also establish many lifelong friendships. Students may still belong to clubs, but they must learn to work all things into their schedules. Being editor of our high school yearbook has not prevented me from working on a project. Even though it may be frustrating, don't quit.

AWARDS

Junior High School
　1. Centenary Region I Science Fair (1963)
　　　First Place, Junior Physical Division
　2. Centenary Region I Science Fair (1964)
　　　Second Place, Junior Biological Paper Division
Senior High School
　1. Centenary Region I Science Fair (1965)
　　　First Place, Senior Biological Division
　　　U.S. Army Award
　　　Outstanding Girls Project
　2. Centenary Region I Science Fair (1966)
　　　First Place, Senior Biological Division
　　　Outstanding Girls Project
　　　$2000 scholarship to Centenary College, Shreveport, La.
　3. International Science Fair (1966)
　　　Second Award